*The Camera Lucida
in Art and Science*

William Hyde Wollaston. An engraving by William Skelton from a painting by John Jackson, RA. This portrait, inscribed to the Duke of Sussex, was published after Wollaston's death.

The Camera Lucida
in
Art and Science

John H Hammond

Ministry of Agriculture,
Fisheries and Food (retired)

and

Jill Austin

School of Environmental Sciences,
University of East Anglia

Adam Hilger, Bristol

British Library Cataloguing in Publication Data

Hammond, John H.
    The camera lucida in art and science.
    1. Camera lucida——History
    I. Title   II. Austin, Jill
    681′.41   NC730

ISBN 0-85274-527-3

Consultant Editor: **Professor A J Meadows,**
                Loughborough University

Published under the Adam Hilger imprint by IOP Publishing Ltd
Techno House, Redcliffe Way, Bristol BS1 6NX, England

Printed in Great Britain by J W Arrowsmith Ltd, Bristol

*For our
Parents and
Friends*

Contents

Introduction

The camera lucida, a diminutive sketching aid invented in 1806, enjoyed considerable popularity among artists and scientists throughout the nineteenth century. In the art world it declined to almost total obscurity by the 1930s, and although still used in microscopy it has suffered a name change. There was little doubt that the camera lucida would soon have become a curiosity briefly mentioned in encyclopaedias and frequently misunderstood in art histories.

It was against this background that we set out to record the origin of the camera lucida from which a variety of instruments was developed, and which collectively provide a fascinating, though short-lived, history.

The name camera lucida when translated from the Latin bears no relation to the instrument. Although the Latin plural was used on very rare occasions we have followed the majority practice of treating camera lucida as an English name, with an added s, camera lucidas, for the plural.

Acknowledgments

For the greater part of the material and information which went into the making of this book we are grateful for assistance from our friends at the Science Museum and the Science Museum Library, South Kensington, especially the staff of the Library who are ever generous of their time, and to Judith Brody and Rosemary Hartnett for translations. Our thanks are also due for assistance at the British Library, the Patent Office and the Science Reference Library, and the libraries of the Royal Society, the Royal Institute of British Architects and the City of London Guildhall. We are grateful for cooperation received at the Museum of the History of Science, Oxford, the Whipple Museum of the History of Science, Cambridge, the Royal Scottish Museum, Edinburgh, and the Royal Ontario Museum, Toronto. For correspondence about John Sell Cotman our thanks go to the Castle Museum, Norwich, and Dr Miklos Rajnai of Messrs Sotheby, and we owe thanks to Dr Michael Pidgley for useful discussions about artists. We are grateful for discussions with Mr Ralph Hyde, at the Guildhall Print Room, about Thomas Hornor, and with Mr R Walker, at the National Portrait Gallery, about Sir Francis Chantrey.

We are conscious of many persons who, during our researches, offered notes and suggestions, and we wish to thank them all for their help and encouragement.

We are also indebted to Neville Hankins of Adam Hilger, whose friendly tolerance and enthusiasm concluded a long gestation period and brought about this book.

Acknowledgments

Thanks are due to the following for permission to reproduce illustrations:

British Library
British Micropalaeontological Society
British Museum
Messrs Christie
Professor J L Cloudsley-Thompson
Mr R S Key
Messrs Leitz
Royal College of Physicians
Royal Microscopical Society
Royal Ontario Museum, Toronto
Royal Society
Science Museum, London (Crown Copyright)
Miss Anna Tait
Whipple Museum of the History of Science,
    Cambridge

Part One

The Sketching Instrument

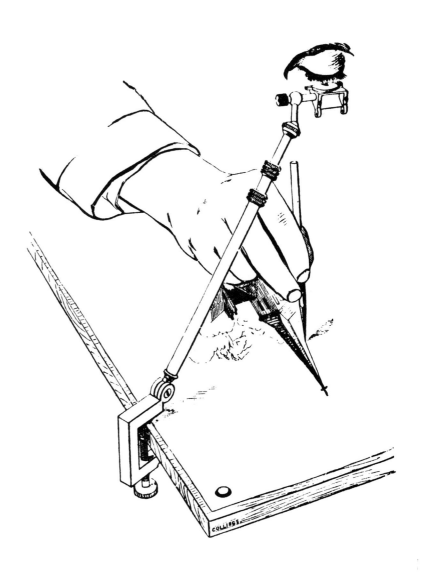

Illustration overleaf from Stanley W F 1925. *Drawing and Mathematical Instruments*.

William Hyde Wollaston and the Invention of the Camera Lucida

William Hyde Wollaston, born 1766, died 1828, chemist, metallurgist, optician, physiologist. Such are the bare prosaic facts of one of the last great natural philosophers—the man who discovered how to work platinum, wrote about fairy-rings and refraction, and invented the camera lucida. William's father, the Reverend Francis Wollaston (1731–1815), was interested in astronomy and compiled a catalogue of stars. He became a Fellow of the Royal Society, and in 1758 married Althea Hyde. In 1762 they moved from Althea's comfortable home in Charterhouse Square, London, to the country rectorship of East Dereham, near Norwich. In his essay on William Wollaston, Dr Henry King wrote, 'Francis planned a large family and felt that it would best flourish in a country setting'.[1] Whether planned or not it was certainly large, William was the third child—fourteen more were to follow.

At an early age William was sent to a private school at Lewisham near London, moved to Charterhouse at the age of eight and went from there to Cambridge. He entered Caius College in 1782, at the age of sixteen, as a scholar, eventually becoming a Fellow and finally a Bachelor of Medicine in 1788. In the following year William had his first appointment as a physician at Huntingdon but he very soon moved to a practice at Bury St Edmunds where he stayed until 1797. During the course of his duties he met Henry Hasted, the relative of a patient. Wollaston and Hasted were to become lifelong friends, though they were most together at Bury within a circle of young acquaintances enjoying country walks, rides and shooting parties.

William's manner and skill as a physician was highly acclaimed by his friends who felt he deserved greater recognition and that he should obtain a practice in London. Yet it seems from Hasted's account[2] that the seeds of Wollaston's scientific career were sown during the Bury period. However, William moved to London and set up a practice in Cecil Street off the Strand but, Hasted wrote, '... trifling cases, or imaginary ills he was not inclined to attend to, serious ones gave him pain ...'. It appears he was over sympathetic towards suffering and would occasionally weep with pity for a patient. In 1800 he abandoned medicine and, after a short holiday with Henry Hasted, he set himself up as a research chemist. So, from being a practising physician, he became Dr Wollaston the Chemist.

Within five years he had discovered how to make platinum malleable. This precious metal became vitally important for making crucibles and vats in the growing chemical industry. By this time, 1805, he was already a Fellow of the Royal College of Physicians and a Fellow of the Royal Society, of which he was to become Secretary and frequently Vice-President. In spite of Wollaston's very considerable amount of research, his financial success (he left a fortune of about £250 000) and his status in the science of the day he has not excited a biographer; perhaps because his lifestyle was unexceptionable. However, there are essays and reminiscences, and there was a great sense of loss in the scientific world when he died of a brain tumour in 1828.

Whilst on a walking tour with Henry Hasted during the brief period between medicine and chemistry, Wollaston and his friend attempted to make drawings of the scenery. The results were disappointing. Hasted later wrote:

We could only take the outline of the districts, for neither of us could draw well, and we lamented our not being able to do so. Calling on him a few months afterwards in town, I found him with a minute truncated and half-silvered prism fastened with sealing wax to a piece of wire. 'Look' said he 'Here is the very thing we wanted at the Lakes', and very soon came forth that elegant and very useful little instrument the 'camera lucida'.

Hasted said 'a few months afterwards' so the incident would have been either late 1800 or early 1801.

Whilst working on the important platinum project Wollaston wrote a paper on optics, 'A method of examining refractive and dispersive Powers, by prismatic reflection' which was read to the Royal Society on 24 June 1802.[3] His paper of interest for our present subject came the following year, 'On an Improvement in the Form of Spectacle Glasses'[4] in which Wollaston recommends the meniscus form of lens (of which our

Wollaston's illustration for his camera lucida patent specification.

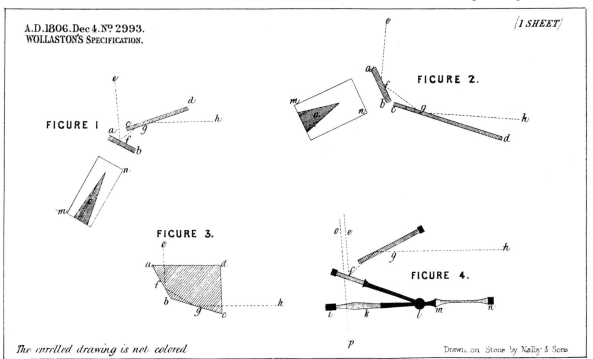

A.D.1806.Dec 4.Nº 2993.
WOLLASTON'S SPECIFICATION.

[1 SHEET]

FICURE I.

FICURE 2.

FICURE 3.

FICURE 4.

The enrolled drawing is not colored.

Drawn on Stone by Malby & Sons

5

spectacles are made today) instead of the bi-convex lenses commonly used at the time. Unfortunately the paper received considerable opposition from William Jones, a highly respected optician of the firm W & W Jones.[5] However, Peter Dollond of P & J Dollond made the new spectacles under patent, although they cost about three times as much as ordinary spectacles with bi-convex lenses. Our main concern with the paper is Wollaston's last paragraph, in which he gives a name to the spectacles. 'The opportunity afforded by these glasses of *looking round* at various objects, it is thought may not improperly be expressed by the name of *Periscopic Spectacles*.'

In 1806 a Patent No 2993[6] was granted to William Hyde Wollaston for 'An Instrument whereby any person may draw in Perspective, or may Copy or Reduce any Print or Drawing'. The words 'camera lucida' do not appear anywhere in the specification.

In June of the following year, 1807, Wollaston published similar articles with the title, 'Description of the Camera Lucida' in the *Philosophical Magazine*[7] and the *Journal of Natural Philosophy, Chemistry and the Arts*.[8] There is no explanation, and there are no clues, as to why the term 'camera lucida' was chosen. The slight differences between the two articles amount to no more than editorial assertiveness. A statement at the end of both articles says that it had been advisable to obtain an exclusive sale, by patent, of the camera lucida and Mr Newman of 24 Soho Square had the present disposal of it. In the following issue of the *Journal of Natural Philosophy* there was a corrective notice, 'The Camera Lucida in our Journal, No. 71, p. 1. is sold not only by Mr. Newman, but also by Messrs. P. and G. Dollond, St. Paul's Church Yard.'

In the article (hereafter referred to as the 'Description') the camera lucida is introduced by the explanation that if one looks down onto a sheet of paper through a piece of clear glass inclined at 45° one sees a reflection. Wollaston wrote, 'I might then take a sketch

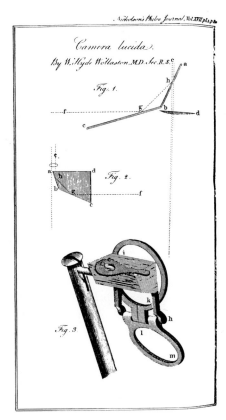

The illustration to Wollaston's article 'Description of the camera lucida' published in *Journal of Natural Philosophy, Chemistry and the Arts*, June 1807. The article was simultaneously published in *The Philosophical Magazine*.

of it. . .'. But, as Wollaston remarked, the position of the objects would be reversed. In order to obtain a correct view he said, '. . . it is necessary to have two reflections. The transparent glass must for this purpose be inclined to the perpendicular line of sight only the half of 45° ($22\frac{1}{2}$°), that it may reflect the view a second time from a piece of looking glass [mirror] placed beneath it, and inclined upwards at an equal angle.' The view will be seen reflected on the clear glass and at the same time the paper and pencil are seen through the glass. It is now possible to make a correct drawing by tracing the reflection. This is a 'see-through' type of camera lucida but Wollaston did not offer it as an instrument for drawing, he wrote this part of the Description merely as an explanation for the principle of his four-sided prism.

Two sides of the prism are at the same angle to each other as the clear glass and mirror, 135°, consequently the view is reflected twice within the prism and the total internal reflection is much more brilliant than an external reflection from a mirror or clear glass. 'But', Wollaston wrote, 'when the prismatic reflector is employed, since no light can be transmitted directly through it, the eye must be so placed that only a part of its pupil may be intercepted by the edge of the prism. The distant objects will then be seen by this portion of the eye, while the paper and pencil are seen past the edge of the prism by the remainder of the pupil.' This is a 'split-pupil' camera lucida. An eyeshade with a hole was provided. The hole was positioned over the edge of the prism to provide the split pupil, while the exact position of the hole was adjusted so the same amount of light was received from the view and the paper. If this was not the case, only the brighter image could be seen. Experienced users of the camera lucida learned to do without this eyeshade and continuously adjusted the position of their eye as the balance of light changed across the scene being drawn.

In later years opticians devised many forms of

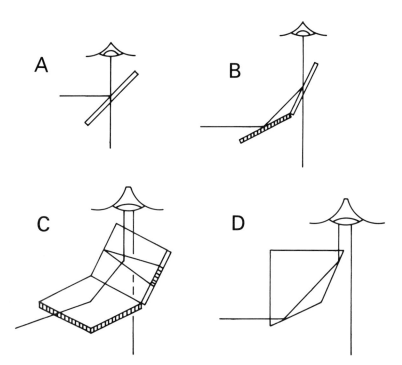

A: a simple camera lucida consisting of a piece of glass at 45°, a drawing made with this single reflection would be reversed left to right. B: a 'see-through' camera lucida. The light from the object is reflected from a mirror to a clear glass through which the artist also sees the drawing paper and pencil. A correct drawing results from the double reflection. C: a 'split-pupil' camera lucida in which the light from the object is reflected from a mirror to a slim triangle of mirror on a clear glass. An artist uses part of the eye to look at the reflection and the other part to see through the clear glass to the drawing paper. D: Wollaston's four-sided prism, a split-pupil camera lucida. The light from the object is reflected twice within the prism, the artist must observe the reflection through half the eye's pupil and the drawing paper with the other half.

Drawings made with camera lucidas B, C and D are upright and correct left to right.

---

camera lucidas but they all conform to either the 'see-through' type where the artist sees his or her paper and pencil through a reflection, or the 'split-pupil' type in which the reflection is observed with half the pupil and the other half sees the paper and pencil. The brain fuses the two images so that the reflection appears to be on the paper. The terms 'see through' and 'split pupil' will be used to denominate subsequent camera lucidas.

With both forms the eye has to look at two objects, the landscape and the drawing paper, which are at different distances. Wollaston was aware of this difficulty and solved it by means of the addition of simple spectacle lenses. In the 'Description' Wollaston wrote,

> The pencil, however, and any object which it is to trace cannot both be seen distinctly in the same state of the eye, on account of the difference of their distances, and the efforts of successive adaption of the eye to one or the other, would become painful if frequently repeated. In order to remedy this inconvenience, the paper and pencil may be viewed through a convex lens of such a focus as to require no more effort than is necessary for seeing the distant objects distinctly. These will then appear to correspond with the paper in *distance* as well as *direction*, and may be drawn with facility, and with any desired degree of precision.

Returning to Wollaston's patent specification we find that he described a see-through camera lucida which can also be made as a split-pupil type, these are shown in the patent drawing Figs. 1 and 2. Wollaston referred to a mirror reflecting a view to a piece of clear glass from whence it is reflected to the artist's eye, while the artist is able at the same time to see through the reflection. If the illumination of the view is low the clear glass should be replaced by a transparent dark coloured glass which gives a stronger reflection. But it is better for the clear glass to be partly silvered '. . . to allow the paper to be seen through an opening in the silvering or past the edges . . . by one portion of the eye, while the doubly reflected object is seen in the silvering by the other portion of the same eye'.

So far as we are aware, neither of these camera lucidas was manufactured in Wollaston's name and he did not mention them as possible constructions in his 'Description'. Wollaston is associated only with his four-sided prism and they remain inseparable throughout the literature. However, as we shall see later, his 'see through' suggestions of both clear and tinted glasses were taken up by many instrument makers and microscopists in the following years.

The 'Description' closed with a comparison of the camera lucida and the camera obscura. The latter, Wollaston said, was too large to be carried with convenience, objects away from the centre of view were more or less distorted and the field of view was limited to 30° or at most 35°. Whereas the camera lucida was small and portable, there is no distortion and 'as much as 70° or 80° might be included in one view'. In fact it is not quite a true comparison. If a supplementary lens has to be used with a camera lucida there will be some distortion of a similar nature, though possibly not so great as with a camera obscura. The wide angle of view, 70° or 80° which Wollaston claimed, can only be achieved by pivoting the prism. This upsets the balance of the illumination and the split-pupil effect becomes extremely difficult to manoeuvre. In his comparison of the two instruments and his claims for the camera lucida we suggest that Wollaston was misleading to the extent of salesmanship. The camera obscura and camera lucida are examined later in more detail on pp. 78–80.

In 1812, five years after the publication of the 'Description', Wollaston read a paper to the Royal Society 'On a Periscopic Camera Obscura and Microscope'.[9] At the end of his lecture he referred to the camera lucida.

Beside the foregoing instances of the adaption of periscopic principles, I should not omit to notice their application to the camera lucida; as there is one variety in its form, that was not noticed in the description which I originally gave of that instrument. In drawing, by means of the camera lucida, distant objects are seen by rays twice reflected, at the same time and in the same direction that rays are received from the paper and pencil by the naked eye . . . But since an eye that is adjusted for seeing the paper and pencil, which are at a short distance, cannot see more distant objects distinctly without the use of a concave glass, it may be assisted in that respect by a due degree of concavity given to either or both the transmitting surfaces of the prism. It is, however, to the upper surface alone that this concavity is given, for since the eye is then situated on the side toward the centre of curvature, it receives all the benefit that is proposed from the periscopic principles.

Even to the Royal Society Wollaston gave no explanation for his use of the term 'camera lucida'.

At the Whipple Museum of the History of Science, Cambridge, there is an 'Original model in wood of Wollaston's Camera Lucida' which is said to be Wollaston's own. The Cambridge Philosophical Society held an exhibition of historic scientific apparatus at Cambridge in 1936,[10] the catalogue entry states: '119a. Camera Lucida. ?1786, 1807. Cavendish Laboratory. Wollaston's Original Model in wooden frame. A label '1786' may indicate the date of the invention though it was not put on the market until 1812.' This entry was copied by Gunther who added a drawing for his book *Early Science in Cambridge*.[11]

Whether this apparatus is an original model, a prototype or was Wollaston's own is hard to decide, but questions may be posed. In 1786 Wollaston was at Cambridge with the intention of becoming a physician. Fourteen years later we have the first intimation of a drawing aid and six years afterwards the Patent. It is difficult to accept Wollaston abandoning a project for twenty years or even the fourteen when he and Hasted went to the Lakes. We know from the 'Description' in 1807 that the camera lucida was on the market before 1812. Unlike Gunther's drawing the model is extremely crude, somehow not in keeping with the meticulous manner of a man whose laboratory might be on a tea tray.

Most mystifying of all is the front surface of the

The camera lucida which is said to be Wollaston's prototype. It is now at the Whipple Museum of the History of Science, Cambridge. The apparatus is shown here approximately full size, 9.5 cm long.

prism which is convex, the focal length is estimated at 50 mm (2 inches). The only part which agrees with Hasted's description is that the prism is held in place by *sealing wax*. Perhaps we should look at the 'Description' again. Wollaston wrote (1807) 'Having a short time since amused myself with attempts to sketch various interesting views without an adequate knowledge of the art of drawing... I am in hopes that the instrument, which I contrived for this purpose, may be acceptable even to those who have attained to greater proficiency in the art... The principles on which it is constructed will probably be most distinctly explained by tracing the successive steps, by which I proceeded in its formation.' The 'various interesting views' accords with Hasted's account of their holiday in the Lakes in 1800.

How Wollaston arrived at the construction of the camera lucida is a matter of hearsay. Dr King, referring to Paris's *Life of Sir Humphrey Davy*, says that he observed certain effects in a cracked mirror when shaving.[12] The reference is a footnote on page 148 of the two-volume edition (it was deleted for the single-volume edition). Paris wrote, 'I have lately been informed that the idea of constructing an instrument like the Camera Lucida, first suggested itself to Dr. Wollaston, on his noticing certain phenomena occasioned by a crack in the glass before which he was shaving himself.'[12] In the 'Description' Wollaston wrote 'The principles on which it is constructed will probably be most distinctly explained by tracing the successive steps, by which I proceeded in its formation.' This was followed by his observation of a reflection on a clear sheet of glass and at the same time seeing through the glass. We may be certain that he had noted, and was interested in, reflections on and in clear glass earlier than 1802 when his paper concerning a refractometer was published.[3]

Why was the camera lucida so called? It is not mentioned in the Patent and it is not formally named in the 'Description' as the Periscopic Spectacles were in the 1803 paper. We have no clues except possibly a sentence in the 'Description'—'Since the primary intention of this instrument is already in some measure, answered by the Camera Obscura, a comparison will naturally be made between them.' As an instrument, and when translated from the Latin, a 'camera obscura' is a 'dark room' or a 'dark box' but a lens is an essential requirement. 'Camera lucida' when translated is a 'light room' or 'light box', as an instrument it has no box and does not require a lens. It is possible that at the beginning of the nineteenth century the term 'camera obscura' was well on the way to losing its Latin origin and was becoming accepted as an English name for a drawing instrument; the word 'camera' being operative for 'drawing'. This conjecture suggests that Wollaston thought of the 'camera obscura' as 'drawing in the dark' as indeed one does with a tent or book-form camera obscura, and the box reflex type requires a hood over the drawing area. Whereas with the camera lucida drawing is done in the light. Whatever the reason for the name 'camera lucida' it has caused a good deal of confusion, particularly with a publication by Robert Hooke.

In the *Philosophical Transactions* 17 August 1668 the first item is 'A contrivance to make the Picture of anything appear on a Wall, Cup-board, or within a Picture-frame, &c., in the midst of a Light room in the day-time; or in the Night-time in any room that is enlightened with a considerable number of candles; divised and communicated by the Ingenious Mr. Hook, as follows; This optical Experiment, here to be described, is New, though easy and obvious; and hath not, that I know, been ever made by any other person this way.'[13] Hooke explained how to illuminate an object by reflecting sunlight on to it with mirrors then with a 'broad Convex-glass' to project an image of the object 'to appear upon the walls of a Light room'. The paper ends 'So far our Inventor; who hath not contented himself with the bare speculation, but put the same in practice some years since, in the presence of several members of the R. Society, among whom the Publisher had the good fortune to see the successful performance of what is here delivered.'

By illuminating an object with sunlight and using a large-diameter lens Robert Hooke was projecting an image in a room without drawing the curtains or closing the shutters—a light room. The room itself was not an instrument as a 'Darke Roome' was a camera obscura.[14] We must remember that rooms in seventeenth-century houses were not very large, the windows also were small and a projected image, however poor by our standards, was, if at all discernible, a source of wonder and delight. However, Wollaston called his instrument 'camera lucida', whilst Robert Hooke had used the phrase 'a Light room', and one is a translation of the other.

During the nineteenth century the classics were still

the mainstay of an academic education, and there is little doubt that compilers of dictionaries and encyclopaedias were classicists. Consequently under the heading 'Camera Lucida' almost every dictionary of the last century referred to Dr Hooke followed by Dr Wollaston. However, the confusion is not entirely due to Wollaston's inept choice of 'camera lucida' for his drawing instrument, there is a pre-1806 reference to the term. Charles Hutton's *Mathematical and Philosophical Dictionary* of 1795 records 'Camera Lucida, a contrivance of Dr. Hook to make the image of anything appear on a wall in a light room; either by day or night. see Phil. Trans. 38, p. 741.'[15] Surely only a pedant would translate English into Latin for an English dictionary! However, there are recent examples: Waterhouse (1909) '. . . there is a somewhat vague description by Hooke of a "Camera Lucida" or "contrivance to make a picture . . ."' and Gernsheim (1955) 'This arrangement which Hooke called "camera lucida". . .'.[16,17]

Encyclopaedias are a long time in the making which may account for *Encyclopaedia Londinensis* (1810) and Rees' *Cyclopaedia* (1819) mentioning only Robert Hooke.[18,19] Perhaps the most interesting is *Encyclopaedia Metropolitana* (1845) which had two entries for camera lucida.[20] In the Optics section Wollaston's was described almost as fully as in his own 'Description' followed by a separate entry 'Dr. Hooke's camera lucida, or megascope. Dr. Hooke's apparatus, which we have seen described under the name of camera lucida, but which appears to us to answer better to the second denomination of megascope. . .'. A megascope was a type of camera obscura. Some editors just blundered their way through the problem, for instance Knight's *Practical Dictionary of Mechanics* (1877) said the camera lucida was 'Founded upon the invention of Baptista Porta (1589), by Dr. Hooke about 1674. Improved by Wollaston, 1805. Phil. Trans. 38 p. 741.'[21]

15

From Kepler *Dioptrice* 1611.

XIV.   PROPOSITIO. PROBLEMA.

Vmbras contra Solem projicere.

Præstat hoc Cubus Crystallinus. Sit enim F O cubus & B β Sol. A ω corpusculum in superficie cubi F A. Radÿ igitur B A, β ω, qui umbram extrinsecus ambientes formant, refringuntur in A C, ω x. Et C A, x ω necessariò plus quàm 48°. eleuantur supra puncta superficiei A ω, per IX. Cum autem angulus Cubi A F C sit rectus, & C A F sit plus quàm 48°; erit F C A minus quàm 42°. Plus igitur quàm 48°. & sic plus e- tiam quàm 42°. inclinantur A C & ω x. à vertice superficiei C F. Qua- re per XIII. A C ω x non penetrabunt superfici- em F C. Quare per Optica principia, toti reper- cutientur in O D superficiem, & angulis quidem æqualibus A C F, D C O. Et quia C O D angulus cubi rectus est, & D C O (æqualis ipsi A C F) mi- nor quàm 42°. igitur C D O plus erit, quàm 48°; minus igitur quàm 42°, inclinatur à vertice su- perficiei D O ; ideoq́ exire potest in E; Sic x δ in ε. Et sic umbra ipsius A ω cadit in E ε contrario situ, sitq́ Soli propior quàm corpus A ω, longius productis D E, δ ε.

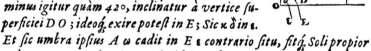

Eodem modo demonstrari potest, si in ω collocetur erecta turricula, ω θ, umbræ culmen E contra Solem conversum iri.

We have also found a reference claiming priority of invention of the camera lucida for Kepler. Obviously this was very exciting; however, it proved erroneous.

Heinrich Schwarz wrote in *Pantheon* (1966), 'Actually, these two men [Wollaston and Amici] intro- duced and improved for practical use the camera lucida two hundred years after it had been invented and clearly described by Johannes Kepler. In his 'Diop- trice', first published in Augsburg in 1611, Kepler gives an exact description of the camera lucida...'.[22] Schwarz's reference led to the XIV Propositio. Problema of Kepler's *Dioptrice* and the comment by Caspar and Hammer.[23,24]

Caspar and Hammer's comment—'Ob man Kepler mit E. Hoppe (Geschlichte der Optik, Leipzig 1926, S. 27) als Erfinder de Camera lucida bezeichen dorf, scheint froglich; diese eine Anwendung der Total-reflexion durfte dafur Kaum genugen.'—can be translated as 'It is doubtful whether one should follow E. Hoppe (Geschlichte der Optik, Leipzig 1926, S. 27) in claiming that Kepler should be seen as the inventor of the *Camera lucida*; this single use of total internal reflection is hardly adequate to support such an inference.'†

It should be noted that Kepler's *Dioptrice* is largely a series of abstract mathematical exercises set out in the Euclidean manner. Many of the Problems, as No XIV (To make shadows against the Sun) had no practical purpose at the time.

Perhaps the most satisfactory explanation for the name 'camera lucida' comes from the *Penny Cyclopaedia* (1836).

> Camera Lucida and Camera Obscura, the light and dark chamber, a name given to two methods, very like in principle of throwing images of external objects upon a plane or curved surface, for the purpose of drawing or amusement. In the first contrivance there is no *chamber*, but as it was the last invented, and as its predecessor had been called *camera obscura*, it was called *camera lucida*.[25]

Nothing could be more simple.

References

Further information about the life and works of William Hyde Wollaston may be found in:
Dictionary of National Biography (1900)
Dictionary of Scientific Biography (1970)
Gentleman's Magazine supplement to vol. 99 (1829) obituary
Wilson G 1862 *Religio Chemici*

1. King H C 1954 Life and optical work of W. H. Wollaston *British Journal of Physiological Optics* **11** 10–31
2. Hasted H 1849 Reminiscences of Dr. Wollaston *Proceedings of the Bury and West Suffolk Archaeological Institute* **1** 121–34
3. Wollaston W H 1802 A method of examining refractive and dispersive powers by prismatic reflection *Philosophical Transactions of the Royal Society* **92** 365–80 Pl. 14

†We are indebted to Dr Judith Field for this translation.

4. Wollaston W H 1803 On an improvement in the form of spectacle glasses *Philosophical Magazine* **18** 143–6

5. Correspondence from W H Wollaston, W Jones and E Walker in the *Journal of Natural Philosophy, Chemistry and the Arts* 1804 **7** 192–8, 241–2, 291–4 and in the *Philosophical Magazine* **18** 143–6, 165–6

6. Wollaston W H 1806 An instrument whereby any person may draw in perspective, or may copy or reduce any print or drawing *British Patent* No 2993

7. Wollaston W H 1807 Description of the camera lucida *Philosophical Magazine* **27** 343–7 Pl. 8

8. Wollaston W H 1807 Description of the camera lucida *Journal of Natural Philosophy, Chemistry and the Arts* **17** 1–5 Pl. 1

9. Wollaston W H 1812 On a periscopic camera obscura and microscope *Philosophical Transactions of the Royal Society* **102** 370–7

10. Cambridge Philosophical Society June 1936 *Catalogue of a Loan Exhibition of Historic Scientific Apparatus in Cambridge* p. 20

11. Gunther R T 1937 *Early Science in Cambridge* (Oxford: Oxford University Press) p. 109

12. Paris J A 1831 *Life of Sir Humphrey Davy* 2 vol. edn p. 148

13. Hooke, Robert 1668 A contrivance to make the picture of any thing appear on a wall . . . of a light room etc *Philosophical Transactions of the Royal Society* No 38 741–3

14. Aubrey, John 1978 John Dee *Brief Lives* ed O L Dick (Harmondsworth: Penguin) p. 249

15. Hutton, Charles 1795 *A Mathematical and Philosophical Dictionary*

16. Waterhouse Major Gen. J 1909 Robert Hooke's portable camera obscura *Photographic Journal* **49** New Ser. 33 333

17. Gernsheim H 1955 *History of Photography* (Oxford: Oxford University Press) pp. 77, 93

18. *Encyclopaedia Londinensis* 1810 652–3

19. Rees, Abraham 1819 *Cyclopaedia*

20. *Encyclopaedia Metropolitana* 1845 475–6 Pl. 9

21. Knight E H 1877 *Practical Dictionary of Mechanics* p. 434

22. Schwarz, Heinrich 1966 Vermeer and the camera obscura *Pantheon* **24** 170–8

23. Caspar M and Hammer F 1941 *Johannes Kepler, Gesammelte Werke 1602–1611* vol. 4 (Munich) pp. 358–9

24. Kepler J 1611 *Dioptrice*

25. *Penny Cyclopaedia* 1836 193

The Early Years of Wollaston's Camera Lucida

From the announcement in the *Philosophical Magazine* and the *Journal of Natural Philosophy* of 1807 we may be certain that Wollaston's prism type of camera lucida was being made and sold within a few months, if not weeks, of him receiving the Patent. So far as is known his other designs were never made, though similar camera lucidas of the 'see-through' type soon followed, notably from the French optician Amici and Alexander of Exeter. The instrument makers mentioned by Wollaston were Newman and Dollond.

The camera lucidas were supplied with a sheet of instructions. We have seen two different sheets; both are illustrated but undated, and neither refers to Wollaston.[1,2] One sheet appears to be earlier than the other; it is entitled 'Directions for using the Camera Lucida', the text gives the barest guidance and says 'This instrument is sold by Mr. Newman, No. 24 Soho Square; by Messrs. P. & G. Dollond, St. Paul's Church-Yard; and   '. The blank space after 'and' was probably intended for lesser retailers to write in their names. The second sheet includes 'Mr. W. Cary, 182, Strand' printed after the 'and'. The heading of this sheet is 'The Camera Lucida. An instrument for drawing Objects in true Perspective, and for copying, reducing, or enlarging other Drawings.' The text is more explanatory and helpful for the user. The University Museum at Utrecht has a Wollaston-type

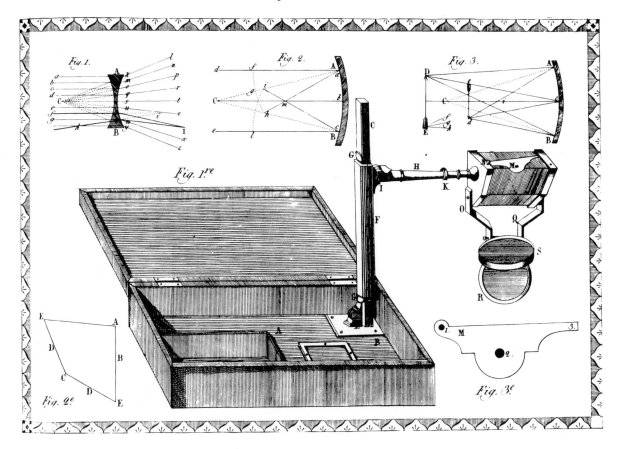

A camera lucida complete with a carrying case which also served
as a stand. From J G A Chevallier *Le Conservateur de la Vue*
(1815).

---

camera lucida in a case, complete with a sheet of
instructions which has the three names Dollond, Newman and Cary.[3] It is interesting to note that Cary was
not one of the initial makers to whom Wollaston gave
manufacturing rights. He had been a maker of astronomical apparatus for Wollaston's father, and he was
handling almost all of Wollaston's platinum transactions—which were often in three-figure sums. Camera
lucidas marked 'Cary' are not uncommon in the sale
rooms. The Science Museum, London, and the Centre
for Photography, Toronto, have specimens.

It is thought that initially, during the early period of manufacture, the prisms were tested or examined. This conjecture arose because one of the camera lucidas at the Science Museum, South Kensington, has the number 3193 scratched directly on the glass. At first sight the number appears to be very high, nevertheless the instrument was made before 1829; it was a gift from Wollaston to his godson, General Sir William Codrington. An unnamed Wollaston-type camera lucida at the Whipple Museum of the History of Science, Cambridge, has the number 1882 scratched on the prism.

Two Wollaston-type prism camera lucidas at the Museum of the History of Science, Oxford, have numbers scratched on the brass housing of the prism; number 906 has 'Patent' stamped on the top of the housing, number 966 is incomplete. Neither instrument has a maker's name.

Chevallier described a camera lucida which he said was due to English opticians.[4] The illustration is of a Wollaston prism camera lucida on an arm attached to a rectangular column with adjustable height. The column is fixed in one corner of a wooden box into which the entire apparatus collapses for carrying.

Annalen der Physik reported Wollaston's 'Description' in 1810 and in 1812 printed a commentary by Professor Ludicke, in which he described his own modification. It is hardly a modification as it is a see-through instrument.[5] Ludicke's 'modification' is described and illustrated on p. 37.

Advice and hints on the use of a camera lucida were published in a letter to *Nicholson's Journal* from R B Bate, at that time an apprentice instrument maker.[6,7] Bate was replying to a letter from T Sheldrake who, through his own incompetence, had been critical of the camera lucida. This correspondence is described in more detail later in the chapter 'Drawing with a Camera Lucida' (p. 81).

The *British Cyclopaedia* described Wollaston's camera lucida at length and quoted from the 'Descrip-

This engraving of Wollaston's prism camera lucida is typical of many illustrations in encyclopaedias, dictionaries and popular books on optics of the last century. From *The London Encyclopaedia* (1829).

tion'.[8] John Good's *Pantologia* devoted considerable space to Robert Hooke's 'camera lucida' but gave only a reference for Dr Wollaston's 'recently invented portable instrument for drawing'.[9] Barlow's *Dictionary* briefly mentioned Hooke and Wollaston with references.[10] Rees' *Cyclopaedia* and *Encyclopaedia Londinensis*, as already mentioned, referred to Robert Hooke only.[11,12]

George Dollond, Optician to His Majesty, at 59 St Paul's Church-Yard, sold a small book entitled 'Description of the Camera Lucida, an instrument for Drawing in true Perspective and for copying, reducing or enlarging other drawings, to which is added, by permission, a letter on the use of the camera, by Capt. Basil Hall, R.N., F.R.S.'.[13] The text consists of four pages of step-by-step instruction on setting up the instrument and seven pages of Captain Hall's letter of advice to the artist. The title page is undated and has no author, but it is thought that it was written by George Dollond himself, and the date of publication must have been after 1828, when Wollaston died. This is made clear in the final statement on the title page, which is also an example of commercial overstatement. After the 'Sold by G. Dollond...' follows 'Who was the sole Manufacture of this Instrument to the Patentee, the late Dr. W. H. Wollaston.' We may wonder whether Dollond was the maker and Newman and Cary were retailers, though shortly we will have reason to doubt whether, in fact, Dollond actually *made* camera lucidas.

At this juncture a comment should be made on the name camera lucida for, as with the camera obscura, it was frequently abbreviated to 'camera'. Having established 'camera lucida' in his essay Dollond continued with 'camera', but reverted to 'camera lucida' in the final paragraph. Captain Hall also followed this practice.

In 1826 the *London Mechanics' Register* featured Wollaston's camera lucida on a front cover, and the

A camera lucida and drawing table. From the price list of Chas. Roberson & Co., artists' colour manufacturers, not dated, London.

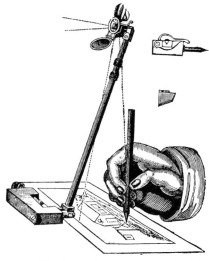

Dr Wollaston's camera lucida. From *The London Mechanics' Register* (1826).

accompanying article gave a full description.[14] A catalogue from the instrument makers Watkins and Hill lists Wollaston's camera lucida at prices from £1.11s.6d. to £2.12s.6d., and portable mahogany folding stands for use with the instrument were from one to three guineas.[15] Francis West wrote a small book, similar to Dollond's, on Wollaston's camera lucida with observations by Captain Basil Hall.[16]

A fascinating and amusing series of letters appeared in the *Mechanics' Magazine* over the period June 1829 to July 1830.[17] The correspondence, in which there were seven participants, was started by a letter about the pantograph and a request for information about the best instrument for copying maps and drawings. 'J' replied 'I am confident that the best is R. Hooke's Camera Lucida.' He proceeded to extol and explain, but without saying so, what is obviously Wollaston's camera lucida. In his last paragraph he wrote 'The camera lucida is constructed upon the principle of the prism, and produces no distortion whatever. It may be purchased ... at Dollonds ... with an accompanying paper of instructions.' 'J.O.B.' was intrigued, he had never seen a camera lucida and he wanted a description with a drawing. 'H.J.' replied at length, two and a half pages, with drawings of Wollaston's camera lucida and drawings made with it; he said it was 'Hooke's Camera Lucida, as improved by Wollaston'. He was misquoting or misunderstanding the *Encyclopaedia Britannica Supplement* of 1824, which, nevertheless, he mentions as his source. 'A Juvenile Reader' was completely mystified and 'wished to know ... the true designation ... because [he wrote] I should prefer having the most useful and complete instrument of the kind ... it seems there are two instruments of the name, one by Dr. Hooke and one by Dr. Wollaston'. Somewhat testily 'H.J.' replied '... I distinctly recollect having written 'Hooke's Camera Lucida *as improved* by Dr. Wollaston'. He continued with a further explanation of the instrument, and a diatribe about engravers reversing

A Wollaston type of camera lucida (figs 1–4). The drawing of the double-action pump was made with the camera lucida (fig. 5). From *The Mechanics' Magazine* (1830).

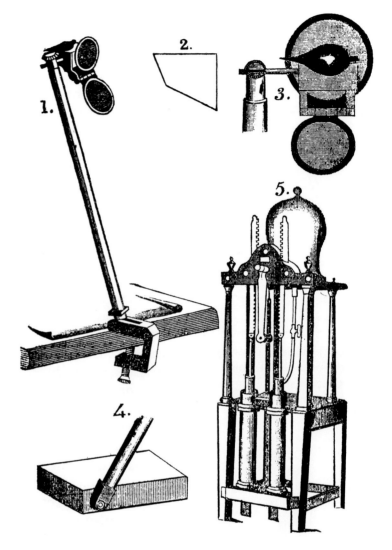

the drawings he had submitted. Wm. Baddley, Jun. had read the correspondence and was induced to buy a camera lucida; he continued by quoting almost the entire article published by the Society for the Diffusion of Useful Knowledge. The final letter had an economic outlook. 'J.E.' said that the praises bestowed upon the camera lucida were not overrated, but he was astonished at the price of the instrument '*as made*★ by Dollond whose prices are from 31s.6d. to *seven guineas!*' He berated the cost of '. . . a brass clamp, a piece of drawn tube, and a glass prism stuck on the end of it . . .'. He closed his letter with '. . . any lapidary will cut a glass prism . . . [and] the brass work . . . may be finished by an ordinary workman, making the expense less than one-third the price of the commonest instrument'. The footnote read '*From good authority, I learn they are all chiefly *made* by an obscure journeyman in the neighbourhood of Whitechapel.'

So much for 'Made by Dollond' and possibly other famous names. It is known that work was frequently contracted-out, and catalogues of optical firms indicate that in the late 1800s prisms of all types were mass produced for the instrument industry.

How easy was the Wollaston camera lucida to construct? Judging by the prolific output of these instruments we must conclude that they presented no problems. The brass mount, eye shade and stem would have been straightforward at the beginning of the nineteenth century; the tiny prism, however, may have presented difficulties. There was no tradition of scientific prism making at the time because this period preceded the rise of spectroscopy. However, we can show that the prism did not need to be accurately made. Measurements were made on five Wollaston prisms in the Science Museum, using a simple contact goniometer from the early nineteenth century. Three early instruments, all with scratched numbers on the prism, and two later instruments, one English and one French, were examined. The tables overleaf give details and the respective dimensions of five Wollaston prisms in camera lucidas at the Science Museum, South Kensington.

The measurement error on the angles was about half a degree, so it was possible to see that the prisms were not optically perfect. However, they were indistinguishable in use when used by one of the authors for sketching. What was unexpected was the similarity in the dimensions of the cross sections of the prisms. For the early instruments this strongly suggests that they were produced by one hand, although sold by different instrument makers. However, it is hard to extend this hypothesis to include the late-nineteenth-century French instrument. Rather, we suggest that the original prisms were simply copied in detail so that the length dimensions were preserved even though it was only the angles which were important. It is quite possible that the workman did not understand the role or use of the prism. We would also like to suggest that the prisms with scratched numbers, and the intervening ones, were made by one hand or workshop.

Item	Scratched number on prism	Camera lucida maker	Inventory number
1	244	—	1980–1832
2	895	—	1912–207
3	3193	—	1980–1831
4	—	Cary	1977–526
5	—	Bouchart	1977–527

(length into the page)

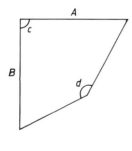

Item	A (mm)	B (mm)	Length (into page)	c (deg)	d (deg)
1	10	8	14	89	131.5
2	10	8	—†	88.5	131
3	10	7	15	90	133
4	11	8.5	—†	91.5	135
5	10	8	19	90	133

†Not possible to measure because of the mount

Finally, it is questionable whether the prisms were ever cut by opticians at all. Brewster mentioned the use of gemstones in connection with Amici's designs (see p. 41) and there were quite a number of lapidaries in London. *Kelly's Post Office Trades Directory* for 1845 listed 29 lapidaries and in the 1855 edition there were

42. Francis West in his instruction book on the camera lucida commented that it required little ingenuity to cut a camera lucida prism with the consequence that many were made cheaply without a good polish by glass cutters and lapidaries. He said of the length of the prism '. . . it has been found that the most desirable one is 11/16 of an inch long'.[16]

When considering the success of the Wollaston camera lucida, we must remember that Wollaston made his living directly from his scientific ventures and his camera lucida was on the market within less than six months of the patent date. Although his four-sided prism may not have been the best theoretical design for a drawing instrument, its construction was very simple and this seems the reason why Wollaston selected it and why the instrument makers produced it in great numbers. It is noticeable that the Wollaston type vastly outnumbers other camera lucidas in museum collections today.

References

1. Science Museum, South Kensington, London
2. Royal Ontario Museum, Toronto, Canada
3. Cittert P H Van 1934 *Descriptive Catalogue of the Microscopes at Utrecht University Museum, Groningen* pp. 106–7
4. Chevallier J G A 1815 *Le Conservateur de la Vue* 257–8 Pl. 10
5. Wollaston W H (translated by von Gilbert, 1810) Beschreibung der Camera Lucida . . . *Annalen der Physik* **34** 355–61 Tab. 1
6. Bate R B 1809 On the camera lucida. letter *Journal of Natural Philosophy, Chemistry and the Arts* **24** 146–50
7. Taylor E G R 1966 *The Mathematical Practitioners of Hanoverian England 1714–1840* (Cambridge: Institute of Navigation/Cambridge University Press) p. 355
8. *British Cyclopaedia* 1809 Optics Pl. 1
9. Good, John M *et al* 1813 *Pantologia*
10. Barlow, Peter 1814 *A New Mathematical and Philosophical Dictionary*
11. Rees, Abraham 1819 *Cyclopaedia*
12. *Encyclopaedia Londinensis* 1810 pp. 652–3

13. Dollond, Geo *Description of the Camera Lucida* nd. 1830?

14. Dr Wollaston's camera lucida 1826 *The London Mechanics' Register* 3 369–71

15. Watkins and Hill 1838 *Catalogue* London

16. West F A 1831 *Description of the Camera Lucida, For drawing in true perspective, the invention of Dr. Wollaston . . . with observations of Captain B. Hall*

17. *Mechanics' Magazine* letters 1829 **2** 303, 381; 1830 **3** 128, 354, 32, 154, 240, 344, 345, 364

The Simple (Single-reflection) Camera Lucida

The introduction to Wollaston's 'Description' states, 'The principles on which it [the camera lucida] is constructed will probably be most distinctly explained by tracing the successive steps, by which I proceeded in its formation. While I look down at a sheet of paper...if I hold between my eye and the paper a piece of plain glass... at... 45°, I see by reflection the view...before me...[and] my paper through the glass. I might then take a sketch of it, but the position of the objects would be reversed.'[1]

So far as we are aware this is the first time that the concept of tracing a reflection had been mentioned. It is surprising, in view of what is to follow, that Wollaston did not actually suggest or even include in his patent the 'piece of plain glass' as an aid for drawing. His final comment 'but the position of the objects would be reversed' presumably condemned the piece of plain glass as a drawing aid. However, there are many occasions when a reversed drawing of a scene is of little consequence in a pictorial composition, whereas for printing purposes reversal is essential.[†]

The first reference we discovered for a camera lucida consisting of a 'piece of plain glass' was in the *Encyclopaedia Britannica Supplement* of 1824 which said that this simplest form may be constructed 'extemporaneously' by fixing on a stand a plain transparent glass or a piece of Muscovy glass at an angle of 45°, a card

†Excepting the modern process of off-set lithography.

with a small hole serving as a sight to keep the eye in one situation.[2] 'Muscovy glass' refers to the laminate Muscovite, a type of mica. This simple camera lucida was repeated in the *Encyclopaedia Britannica* of 1875–89 and again in the 1910 edition which also stated that the image would be 'inverted and perverted', meaning the drawing would be reversed even when turned the right way up.[3,4] This edition of the *Encyclopaedia Britannica* included a diagram of a plain glass camera lucida. The *British Cyclopaedia* (1835) made a similar suggestion for a simple camera lucida and referred to Muscovy glass.[5] The article continued with a full explanation of the prism camera lucida but made no mention of Wollaston.

A simple camera lucida consisting of a vertical pane of clear glass. The artist, when looking at the glass from the same side as the object, saw a reflection of the object together with the paper and pencil through the glass. The drawing was reversed. This apparatus was exhibited by Sir John Robison at the Edinburgh Society of Arts, 8 March 1841. From *The Edinburgh New Philosophical Journal* (1841).

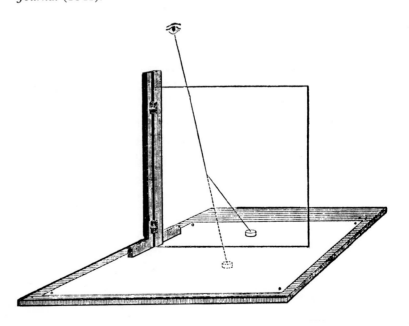

In the *Mechanics' Magazine* of February 1841, 'K.H.' reported a device suggested to him by the Reverend Mr Taylor of York.[6] It consisted of a baseboard with a vertical sheet of glass across the centre. By placing an object 'such as flowers, bulbs, seeds' on one side of the glass a reflection of the object may be seen by looking at the glass from the same side and the paper and pencil through the glass on the other side. A similar device was exhibited at the Edinburgh Society of Arts in March of the same year, 1841, by Sir John Robison, late secretary of the Royal Society of Edinburgh. The meeting, and Sir John's description, were reported with an illustration in the *Edinburgh New Philosophical Journal* and in the *Magazine of Science*, 1841.[7,8] It would be interesting to know the relationship between 'K.H.' and Sir John Robison, for they both mentioned the Reverend Mr Taylor of York, and they used almost exactly the same phrases when describing his suggestion!

S Vecchi, whilst reporting, in 1868, a new camera lucida of his own design which involved two reflections, also mentioned the use of a single clear glass at 45° but so arranged as to reflect the paper and pencil; the object to be drawn was viewed horizontally through the glass.[9] He suggested that a transparent coloured or tinted glass would give a stronger reflection of the pencil point without seriously hindering the artist's vision of the subject. Although Vecchi's arrangement of the glass was different from the camera lucidas we have already mentioned the drawing was still reversed left to right.

A Terquem wrote in 1877 that 'Everyone knows how fatiguing is the prolonged use of the camerae lucidae'.†[10] He found that 'a glass semi-silvered by Foucault and Martin's process can be substituted with great advantage'. Terquem suggested a half-silvered plate of glass 10 × 15 cm at 45° with a sight piece above to avoid parallax by movement of the eye position. He

†One of the rare occasions when the Latin plural was used.

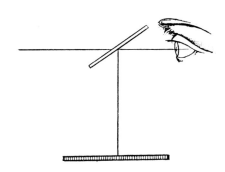

A simple camera lucida which reflected the pencil and drawing paper, the landscape was seen through the glass. From Vecchi S 1868 Una nuova camera chiara *Nuovo Cimento*.

31

said the advantage of his camera lucida over others arose from the use of a large surface which gave a more intense reflection. This was, of course, an erroneous claim.

William Ford Stanley referred in 1888 to the simple form of camera lucida which, he said, may be easily constructed experimentally.[11] He suggested that 'a small piece of tinted plain glass be fixed by any contrivance at the angle of 45 degrees over a sheet of paper . . . the image appears inverted, therefore it does not answer perfectly for sketching; it is, however, much used for scientific purposes, and answers perfectly for sketching the magnified image projected by the microscope or telescope'.† Stanley illustrated a drawing instrument called 'Binko's Spectrograph'—a vertical

---

Pepper's ghost, an illusion entertainment devised by J H Pepper (1821–1900). By means of a sheet of clear glass set at 45° the audience saw a faintly transparent reflection against a scene painted on the backcloth of the stage. In this diagram the lady on the table, unseen by the audience, appeared in the reflection as the goddess Amphitrite in the sea. Appropriate music completed the illusion. From Hopkins A A 1897 *Magic*.

†The use of the word 'projected' is incorrect as will be seen in the section on microscopy.

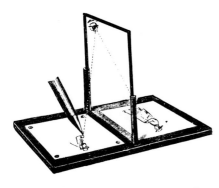

Binko's Spectrograph. A manufactured simple camera lucida similar to the Phantom Line 500 (p. 34). From Stanley W F 1888 *Drawing and Mathematical Instruments*.

sheet of glass on a baseboard, exactly the same as the device described by 'K.H.' and Sir John Robison who got it from the Reverend Taylor in the 1840s! Unfortunately we have not yet discovered whether there was a Mr Binko. The apparatus was described as 'on the Pepper's Ghost Principle' in the 6th edition of 1888.[†] Early editions of Stanley's book are very rare, The British Library editions 1 to 5 being destroyed during the Second World War. However, the Royal Society has a first edition (1866) in which the 'Spectrograph' does not appear. It is also absent in the second edition of 1868, but it does appear in the fifth edition 1878, both the 1868 and 1878 editions being at the Patent Office Library. The 1925 edition of Stanley's book again illustrated the Spectrograph and said it was a sketching instrument formerly introduced as 'a kind of toy'. Indeed, as we shall see shortly, it has returned as a toy.

In 1895 Arthur Harris obtained a patent for an improvement in 'Apparatus for copying drawings and the like'.[12] As in Binko's Spectrograph it consisted of a vertical pane of glass but it was supported above the drawing board which enabled the artist's hand to pass underneath.

The interest in this form of camera lucida was maintained by the engraving, woodblock and lithographic printing processes which required a reversed image on the printing surface. However, the principle of a single transparent reflector was used for purposes other than drawing. Helmholtz in his work on human vision used a sheet of glass at 45° as a comparator.[13] In a similar manner, Margary (1953) made an instrument

Two comparators in which a piece of clear glass was used for observing two subjects at the same time. From H von Helmholtz 1909 *Handbuch der Physiologischen Optik*

[†]For an excellent article on the Pepper's ghost effect the reader should consult the article by Speaight (1963) cited in the main bibliography.

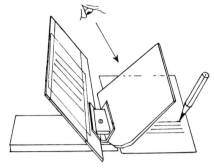

Phantom Line 500. A simple camera lucida for professional use. Made in America and available in England during the 1960s.

for superimposing a pattern such as a texture or weave upon another pattern.[14] In this situation of superimposing one image upon another, the sheet of glass at 45° is referred to as an 'interface' and is frequently used in photographic and television systems. The so called 'head-up' displays for the navigation of aircraft and ships employ a similar device associated with electronic images. The patents of the English Electric Company and Standard Telephones and Cables Ltd, are typical of these applications.[15, 16]

In recent years the pane of glass has been replaced by a sheet of tinted transparent plastic. Sometime during the late 1960s the 'Phantom Line 500' lettering and drawing aid was imported from America by the drawing office suppliers A West & Company.[17] The construction and instructions for use of the device indicate that it was intended for professional commercial artists. The arrangement of the drawing to be copied, the reflector and the copy were at about 60° to each other which allowed a comfortable viewing position for the draughtsman. The instrument is no longer available.

More recently (1983–4) two boxed toys were available, called 'Reflecto-Art' and 'Reflect and Draw', which are modern versions of Binko's Spectrograph.[18,19] Both boxes contain a sheet of tinted transparent plastic with a stand to support it vertically, a set of line drawings, some sheets of plain paper and a few coloured pencils. Everything to hand for a child to start copying. Similar toys were still available in 1986.

Yet another simple single-reflection camera lucida consisted of a small mirror supported by a side arm at 45° above a drawing board. The text and illustration in Varley's 1845 book *Optical Drawing Instruments* indicate that the device may have been manufactured; it was among the items on the Varley stand at the Great Exhibition of 1851.[20] The catalogue entry reads

34

'Reversing camera, by which pictures or objects may be traced the reverse way.' Varley said it was '...a very useful instrument for showing objects or pictures the reverse way, by which they may be etched on copper or drawn on stone for printing the right way'. He explained that the upper edge of the mirror was ground nearly to a knife edge. He said that a drawing to be copied should be fixed upside down whereupon the eye, looking in the mirror, will '...see the drawing erect...on the [drawing] surface and it may be easily traced by letting part of the eye look over the edge of the speculum [mirror] and down on the paper to see the pencil whilst drawing'. When making an enlarged or reduced copy, Varley pointed out that a lens must be placed in front or below the mirror.

The *Library of Useful Knowledge* (1832) also said that 'A very simple one [camera lucida] may be made with a plane reflector, either of speculum metal or plate glass, having its face inclined at an angle of 45°....'.[21]

The popular book by Marion *Wonder of Optics* (1868) referred to making a simple mirror camera lucida and suggested using both eyes when drawing 'and [with] the left eye applied to the mirror the image of the object will be seen on the paper below, and the pencil may be guided with the right'.[22] Marion continued '...the proper use...depends in great measure upon the focus of each eye being the same'. He made no reference to the use of lenses to equalise the distances of object and drawing, but he mentioned the necessity of balancing the light on the object and paper, and suggested whitening the pencil or pen '...so that it may not so easily be lost when drawing the lighted parts of the object'. The article closed with the statement 'we have seen excellent drawings made from plants by means of a little instrument of this kind, which simply consisted of a piece of looking-glass inserted in a cork stuck in a glass bottle'. Unfortunately, Marion did not include one of the excellent drawings from the home-made camera lucida.

References

1. Wollaston W H 1807 Description of the camera lucida. *Philosophical Magazine* **27** 343–7 Pl. 8; also *Journal of Natural Philosophy, Chemistry and the Arts* **17** 1–5 Pl. 1
2. *Encyclopaedia Britannica* 1823 92; *Supplement* 1824 587–9
3. *Encyclopaedia Britannica* 1875–89 740–1 Pl. 34
4. *Encyclopaedia Britannica* 1910 104
5. *British Cyclopaedia* 1835 255–6
6. K. H. 1841 New optical drawing instrument. letter *Mechanics' Magazine* **34** 201–2
7. Robison, John 1841 Notice regarding a cheap and easily used camera lucida, applicable to the delineation of flowers and other small objects. letter *Edinburgh New Philosophical Journal* **30** 402–3
8. A simple camera lucida *Magazine of Science* 1841–2 **3** 204–5
9. Vecchi S 1855–67 Una nuova camera chiara *Nuovo Cimento* **28** 240–6
10. Terquem A 1877 On the employment of a silvered glass as a camera lucida *The London, Edinburgh and Dublin Philosophical Magazine* Ser. 5 **3** 541–3
11. Stanley W F 1888 *Mathematical, Drawing and Measuring Instruments* pp. 155–6
12. Harris, Arthur 1895 Improvements in apparatus for copying drawings and the like *British Patent* No 15 113
13. Helmholtz H von 1909 *Physiological Optics* (translated by J P C Southall, 1924) 3 vols vol. 2 pp. 161, 283
14. Margary A R 1953 A device for demonstrating the appearance of fabrics *British Patent* No 749 463
15. English Electric Co. 1958 Improvements in and relating to navigational aids *British Patent* No 890 791
16. Standard Telephones and Cables Ltd 1960 Improvements in or relating to optical combining arrangements *British Patent* No 906 110
17. Phantom Line 500 Lettering and drawing aid (Phantom Line Graphics Co., Providence, Utah, USA)
18. Reflecto-Art (Interplay (Toys) Ltd Manchester, England)
19. Reflect and Draw (J and L Randall Ltd, Potters Bar, England)
20. Varley, Cornelius 1845 *A Treatise on Optical Drawing Instruments*; also *Official Descriptive and Illustrated Catalogue of the Great Exhibition* 1851 3 vols **1** 436
21. Optical Instruments 1832 *Library of Useful Knowledge, Natural Philosophy* vol. 2 p. 26
22. Marion F (translated by C W Quin, 1868) *Wonders of Optics* pp. 217–23

The 'See-Through' Camera Lucida

In a 'see-through' camera lucida, the light from the object is reflected from a mirror to a clear glass, through which the artist also sees the drawing paper and pencil (see diagram on p. 43). Several opticians used this principle to try and produce an improved camera lucida.

In 1812 *Annalen der Physik* published a commentary by Professor Ludicke, prompted by the German translation of Wollaston's 'Description' (see p. 6), in which he described a 'modified' form of Wollaston's instrument. Ludicke reflected the scene from a silver mirror to a thin piece of clear glass. The two reflecting surfaces were mounted in a box fitted with legs which, judging by Ludicke's illustration, would not permit a very large drawing.

However, the first serious scientific attempts to improve the camera lucida were due to G B Amici.

Giovanni Battista Amici (1786–1863), professor of mathematics at the University of Modena, was wide ranging in his interests which included astronomy, the design of telescopes and microscopes and the growth processes of plants. His remarkable work on the improvement of the microscope began about 1818 and it was at this period that Wollaston's camera lucida caught his attention. In 1819 Amici's own paper on the camera lucida appeared in Italian with a subsequent translation into French in 1823. The translation does not contain the diagrams.[1,2]

Amici admired and praised Wollaston's prism but

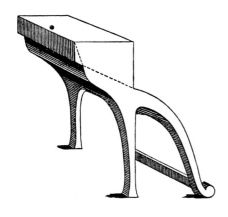

Professor Ludicke's camera lucida. From *Annalen der Physik* (1812).

37

drew attention to its obvious defect—the split pupil. He explained, 'Placing then the pupil close to the face of the prism, in such a manner that it divides the parts equally, one sees at the same time the object, projected on a plane, and the point of the pencil which is intended to follow the contours. It obviously results from this position that, when the segment of the pupil which looks directly at the pencil is large, this appears distinct, while the image which one wishes to copy is feeble, this image on the contrary will appear bright and the pencil obscured, if a greater portion of the eye is looking through the prism. Tiny movements of the eye can cause successive disparities between the image and the pencil and this uncertainty leads to fatigue in the sight of those who are not used to the instrument.' (Author's translation). He went on to say that he purchased a camera lucida in Paris in 1815 from M Dumotiez† for the Cabinet of Physics at the University of Modena. His own improvements were subsequently developed at his own workshop there.

Amici's idea was to have a metal mirror (the metal, usually silver, was coated on one face of a block of glass) inclined at 135° to the plane surface of a sheet of glass with parallel sides. This construction is shown as Fig. 2 in Amici's original illustration. The rays from the object were reflected first from a metallic mirror M and then from the surface of a clear glass at P, the double reflection produced a correct view of the scene for the eye at 0. The pencil was seen directly through the sheet of glass at Q, so this camera lucida was a see-through type. As with the Wollaston prism, lenses were needed to ensure that the object to be drawn and the pencil were the same apparent distance from the eye. Amici pointed out the obvious but useful test for whether the lenses were correctly set up; that there

---

†It was customary to print French names with the courtesy title 'M'. Unfortunately this can lead to confusion; consequently initial letters are given as printed in the original publications.

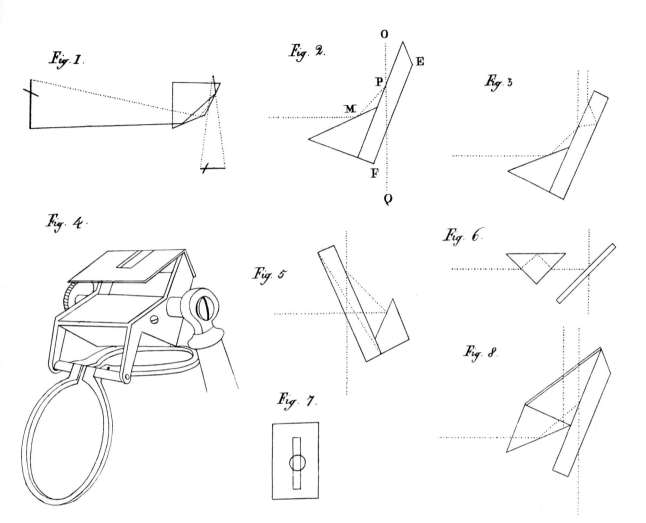

Amici's drawings from his original paper, 'Sopra le camere lucida' 1819. Fig. 4 shows a complete camera lucida with the eyepiece which shielded off unwanted reflections. (The drawings have been re-arranged.)

should be no parallax between the pencil and the object. Balanced lighting was also essential for successful drawing.

So what were the problems with this and Amici's other designs for a camera lucida, all of the see-through type? Amici was remarkably frank about the difficulties and the practical measures needed to overcome them.

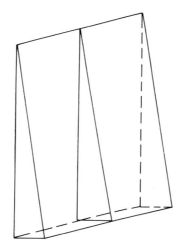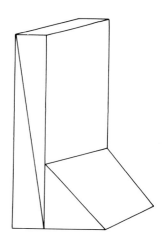

Amici's method for making a piece of glass with parallel faces. A wedge was cut in two and the pieces cemented together. The silvered hypotenuse of a 45° prism made an open angle of 135° with the glass, as Fig. 2 of Amici's original drawings.

First of all there was the problem of a secondary reflection. Amici demonstrated in his Fig. 3 that another reflection was produced at the back surface of the clear glass EF, and although it was weak it tended to confuse the main reflection P. So long as the light rays were parallel, that is coming from a distant object, and the two faces of the piece of glass were perfectly parallel then the two images were coincident to the eye. However, if either of these conditions were violated then a second ghost reflection was seen. Amici remarked that instrument makers experienced great difficulty in producing parallel faces on a sheet of glass. He recommended making a slim wedge of glass and cutting it in half thereby making two identical wedges. One wedge was reversed end to end and cemented on top of the other thus automatically producing a piece of glass with parallel faces. A 45° right-angle prism was cemented by one of its short sides to the glass. The hypotenuse of the prism, which was silvered, then made an angle of 135° to the glass face.

Brewster confirmed the difficulty in obtaining parallel faces on a sheet of glass. He wrote, 'We have constructed these with plates of topaz, which often split with surfaces perfectly polished, and always mathematically parallel... In place of a metallic mirror, we have found small and perfect crystals of ruby, silver, blende, specular iron and oxide of tin much better fitted for this purpose and much easier obtained.'[3]

In order to be able to draw near objects, when the incoming light rays were not parallel, Amici said it was necessary to roughen the back surface of the glass where the unwanted reflection took place. This had to be done little by little whilst making observation with the camera lucida, so that the opaque roughened section did not extend down the glass more than necessary. A further problem was that light rays from an elevated object could be seen by the eye directly from the metallic mirror. This caused yet more confusion because it was a single reflection. A blackened piece of copper with a hole for the eye to look through had to be fitted over the mirror to exclude this reflection. Again this needed careful adjustment.

Amici acknowledged that Wollaston had previously thought of this design but had not pursued it. He illustrated variations on the theme, and according to the anonymous translator of his original paper they were all produced by M Lerebours of Place du Pont-Neuf.[2] Brewster wrote as though he had practical experience of them all, showing preference on different occasions for Fig. 5 and Fig. 8 of Amici's illustration.[3,4]

It must be obvious that ordinary instrument makers were not going to find it easy to mass-produce Amici's instruments. A camera lucida which was produced in the workshop of the top microscopist in Europe was not necessarily going to be a commercial success. And this seems to have been the fate of Amici's designs because his type of camera lucida is now a rarity. There is an example of Amici's Fig. 2 made by Cary in the Science Museum, South Kensington (Inv. No.

Parlour's sketching case. A portfolio containing a drawing board
and a camera lucida which folded
for carrying. From *British Patent*
No 7052 (1836).

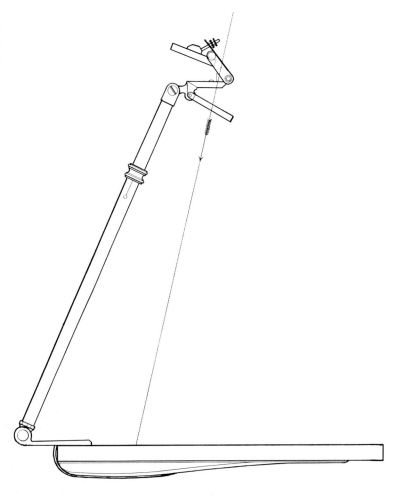

1934–152), but interestingly it is more difficult to use
than a Wollaston type, perhaps because of bad work-
manship.

Samuel Parlour obtained a patent in 1836 for 'Certain Improvements applicable to sketching. . .' which
he called Parlour's Sketching Case.[5] The Sketching
Case consisted of a shallow portfolio about 30 × 25 cm
(12 × 10 inches) containing an attached collapsible
camera lucida and a drawing board. The camera lucida
was of the see-through type, a silvered mirror reflected
the object to be drawn onto a transparent tinted glass.

42

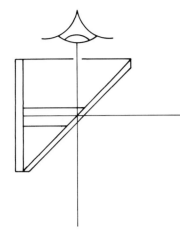

Diagram showing the principle of the Graphic Mirror. Rays from the object pass through a thin glass to a mirror which reflects them back to the glass where they are reflected again and viewed by the artist. The small hole maintains the eye in one position in order to avoid parallax, the apparent relative movement between the reflection and the pencil.

So far as we are aware this was the only complete camera lucida drawing outfit. A small piece of an instrument was found at the Museum of the History of Science, Oxford, with the words 'Parlour's Patent Sketching Case 64' engraved. Comparison with the patent drawing showed the piece to be the frame for the mirror. Unfortunately this is the only evidence we have of the manufacture of Parlour's patent.

Alexander Alexander, an optician and instrument maker, moved from London to Exeter in 1830, where for some fifty years he was in business at No 6 High Street.[6] In 1833 he was appointed optician in ordinary to the King and in 1837 to Queen Victoria. In 1834 the *Exeter and Plymouth Gazette* printed a short note about an instrument '. . . invented by Mr. Alexander . . . for the purpose of facilitating the art of drawing . . . which [he] named the Graphic Mirror'.[7] Alexander's Graphic Mirror, was, perhaps, the most simple and efficient of all camera lucidas. Although more bulky, it is as robust as Wollaston's prism. The only optical components are a mirror, which need not be a surface mirror, and a thin piece of flat glass, both mounted in a brass box. It is a see-through camera lucida and requires no adjustment other than the balance of light on the subject and on the drawing board. The London print dealer, Ackermann, was selling the Graphic Mirror at £1.6s.6d and £2 in a mahogany box.[8] The front cover of the *Magazine of Science* (1840) illustrated the instrument and it was featured in the text along with Wollaston's prism and two of Amici's camera lucidas.[9] The article closed with a full description of the instrument and that it could be seen at Messrs Ackermann's in the Strand. The leaflet

Alexander's Graphic Mirror. This illustration displays the instrument quite well, but the attempt to show it in a working position is unsatisfactory owing to the peculiar perspective chosen by the artist. From *The Magazine of Science and School of Arts* (1840).

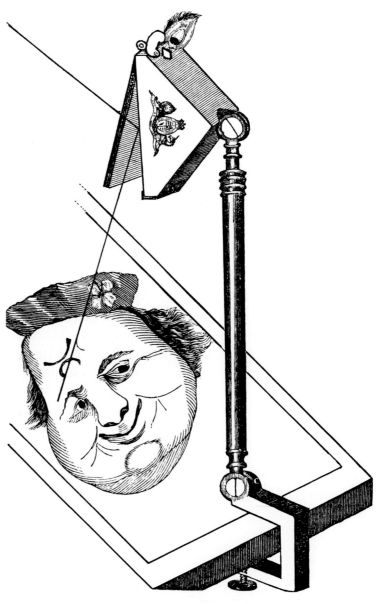

issued with the Graphic Mirror said that 'It can also be used as a Lithographic Delineator for tracing on stone...'.[10] Alexander supplied a piece of tinted glass which fastened to the front of the camera lucida thereby making a triple-reflection instrument. It provided a reversed image for drawing directly on a lithographic stone from which a correct print was made.

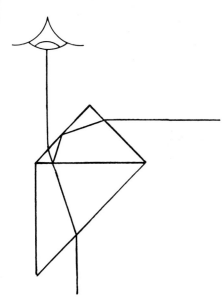

Professor Govi's new camera lucida consisting of two prisms cemented together with a transparent layer of gold between. The metallic layer provided a surface for the second reflection of the scene. From Govi G 1889 *Intorno a una nuova camera-lucida Atti della R. Accademia dei Lincei.*

In 1837 M Kruines presented to the French Academy a new camera lucida consisting of two plates of glass.[11] *Loudon's Architectural Magazine* reported it as from *L'Echo du Monde savant*, 30 August 1837.[12] From the description it appears to have been a see-through design.

During the 1870s G Govi had worked on camera lucida designs for use with the microscope. One construction, the cube, he said would be useful for landscapes and natural history subjects. As the cube presented only one reflection the drawing would be reversed. However, his paper of 1889 described a new and unusual design for a see-through camera lucida.[13] It consisted of two right-angled isosceles prisms, the hypotenuse of one cemented to the cathetus of the other with a thin transparent layer of gold between. The image of the scene was twice reflected in the smaller prism. If this design was ever manufactured it is almost certain to have been by Nachet of Paris. Govi's cube camera lucida was adapted by Lafay for use as a comparator.[14]

M Nachet Jun. reviewed the camera lucidas of Wollaston, Amici and Govi, then offered one of his own design consisting of a fully silvered mirror at 45° to a glass thinly coated with a semi-transparent layer of platinum.[15] Nachet adapted this camera lucida as an ophthalmoscope for Dr Coursserant. The instrument enabled two observers to examine a patient's eye at the same time.

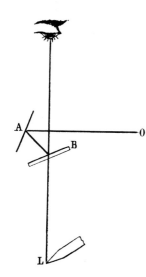

A camera lucida designed by M Nachet Jun. was also constructed as an ophthalmoscope for two observers. The eye in the diagram would be seen by an oculist at positions 0 and L. From Nachet M Jun. 1882 *Nouvelle chambre claire Seances de la Societe Française de Physique.*

Stanley wrote a simple explanation with illustrations of Wollaston and Amici camera lucidas, he said the latter was a modification of Wollaston's.[16] The same explanation and diagrams appeared in Ganot's elementary physics book with the comment that Amici's camera lucida was preferable to Wollaston's.[17]

Alexander's Graphic Mirror was revived in this century in two modern toys. The 'Graphoscope' was a

The Graphoscope. A child's toy of about 1960 made in England. The artist has reversed the direction of the camera lucida in order to make a 'clearer' picture! If it had been drawn correctly the vertical side of the instrument would have merged with the boy's face.

The Magic Art Copier. This camera lucida, of the same principle as Alexander's Graphic Mirror, was made in Taiwan and available in England about 1980. This illustration covered one side of the box which was of this shape and 17.5 cm (7 inches) long, by 3 cm ($1\frac{1}{4}$ inches) deep.

strongly made toy with a camera lucida of the type made by Alexander.[18] The box measured 21 × 16 × 2.5 cm (8 × 6 × 1 inches), it contained the instrument, a ten-page booklet of instructions, sheets of white and black paper and a set of drawings of animals. The Graphoscope was made in England about 1960.

The other toy camera lucida, 'Magic Art', made in Taiwan, is the same principle as the Graphic Mirror and was available about 1980–5.[19] It may still be available. It is extremely flimsy, and was supplied in a soft card box but with satisfactory instructions. There were no paper or specimens, although a piece of black paper was supplied which when folded to stand upright served (inadequately) to shade the drawing area. However, there were time-honoured words of encouragement, 'You may not reproduce the best pictures at first, but with practice you will make great progress.' It was not advertised as a child's toy.

The Edmund Scientific Company of New Jersey deals in 'surplus' electronic and optical components and issues a number of booklets explaining how to make apparatus utilising the parts available.[20] The camera lucida design is the same as Alexander's, it is given the pet name of 'Lucy' in the instructions. Another leaflet from the same firm is titled 'Lucy makes you an Artist!' The construction diagrams are clear and detailed.

It is noticeable today in North America that in many art and design departments optical copying devices are familiarly called 'Lucy'. In fact they are camera obscuras, which in English drawing offices are referred to as 'projectors'.

References

1. Amici G B 1819 Sopra le camere lucide *Opuscoli Scientifici* **3** 25–35
2. Amici G B 1823 Sur la chambre claire *Annales de Chimie et de Physique* **22** 137–55
3. Brewster D 1825 Prof. Amici's improved camera lucidas *Edinburgh Journal of Science* **3** 157
4. Brewster D 1831 Optics—camera lucida *Cabinet Cyclopaedia* pp. 333–5
5. Parlour S 1836 Certain improvements applicable to sketching, drawing or delineating, which I intend to denominate Parlour's Sketching Case *British Patent* No 7052
6. Letter from the Librarian, Central Library, Exeter
7. *Exeter and Plymouth Gazette* 17 Jan., 1 Aug., 1834
8. Ackermann & Co. *Booklist* nd. 1838?
9. *Magazine of Science and School of Arts* 25 Jan. 1840 337–9
10. Alexander, Alexander *The Graphic Mirror* Science Museum, South Kensington, London. Inv. No. 1912–206

11. Optiques—Chambre Claire 1837 *Compte Rendus des Seances de l'Academie des Sciences* **5** 350
12. *Loudon's Architectural Magazine* 1838 276
13. Govi G 1889 Interno a una nuova camera-lucida *Atti della R. Accademia dei Lincei* **5** 3–6
14. Lafay M 1900 Sur deux applications de la chambre claire de Govi *Comptes Rendus des Seances de l'Academie des Sciences* **130** 1122–3
15. Nachet M j 1882 Nouvelle chambre claire *Seances de la Societe Française de Physique* 101–3
16. Stanley W F 1888 *Mathematical, Drawing and Measuring Instruments* pp. 141–6
17. Ganot A 1890 (translated by E Atkinson) *Elementary Treatise of Physics* pp. 603–4
18. The Graphoscope *c.* 1960 (E and S, England)
19. Magic Art. Made in Taiwan with several UK distributors, *c.* 1980. Available from Spencer, London, 1985
20. *Optical Drawing Devices* Popular Optics Library No 9059; also *'Lucy' Makes You an Artist* nd *c.* 1982 (New Jersey: Edmund Scientific Co.)

The Decline of the Camera Lucida

Up until the end of the nineteenth century sketching was not only a pleasant way of recording visual impressions, it was also a highly desirable social accomplishment. A lady was judged by her accomplishments, which included the contents of her portfolio. Many contemporary novelists, including Jane Austen and Charlotte Brontë, bear witness to this. The decline of sketching as a widespread pastime seems to be associated with both the invention of the photographic camera and changing views on education, particularly of women. This change was also responsible for the decline in the use of the camera lucida. Nevertheless, the latter has persisted well into this century and one still comes across isolated examples of its use today.

1840–60

'Caret' wrote to *Notes and Queries* asking for information about his camera lucida made by King of Bristol.[1] He wanted to know how to use it and the meaning of the numbers 2, 3, 4, 5, 7, 10, D engraved on the draw tubes. T B Johnston of Edinburgh replied by quoting from the instruction sheet of his own camera lucida, he did not mention the make. The tubes should be set at D when drawing objects and scenes at a distance, the numbers refer to the distance of near objects in feet and the tube should be set to the corresponding number. The numbers also served as a guide to the scale of reduction or enlargement of the drawing; for instance if an object is two feet from the prism and the drawing paper one foot, the drawing will be half size. When the object is one foot away from the prism and the drawing three feet the drawing will be three times as large as the object. Almost all later camera lucidas were calibrated in this way.

Marbach's *Lexikon* described Wollaston's camera lucida and referred to R B Bate's letter of advice on its use. The *Lexikon* also described, with a very good illustration, Ludicke's camera lucida.[2]

1860–80

Douglas suggested a modification of the type of camera lucida which consisted of a mirror and a clear glass.[3] He found that a thin transparent layer of silver on the second (clear) glass greatly improved the performance. It is quite likely that Douglas made the camera lucidas he described for his own use.

The *American Cyclopaedia, Chambers's Encyclopaedia, Knight's Practical Dictionary* and the *Encyclopaedia of Photography* described only Wollaston's prism, although there were odd references to Robert Hooke.[4,5,6,7] Privat-Deschanel's *Dictionnaire* also described Wollaston's camera lucida and mentioned that there were modifications of it by Amici, Chevalier and Laussedat.[8] *Encyclopaedia Britannica* did not mention Wollaston but fully described the prism and gave the reference for the 'Description'.[9]

1880–1900

All four dictionaries in this period describe only Wollaston's camera lucida; three are illustrated, the fourth, *Haydn's Dictionary*, also mentions Dr Hooke.[10,11,12,13]

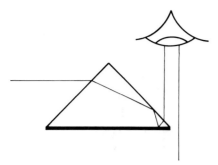

Diagram of the Berville camera lucida which has a normal right-angle prism with a silvered hypotenuse. The image is very bright in this instrument, although the eye has to be close to the prism.

1900–20

Only three references were found for this period. Feldhaus mentioned only Wollaston; Harmsworth referred to Dr Hooke and described the prism with a diagram.[14,15] The *Encyclopaedia Britannica* explained the principle and uses of Wollaston's camera lucida.[16]

1920–40

We have two catalogue leaflets which, though undated, appear to belong to this period. One from P Berville, 25 Rue de la Chaussee-d'Anton, Paris; the other from Lechertier Barbe Ltd, 95 Jermyn Street, St James's, London.[17,18] Both have similar and identical illustrations. The Berville sheet has diagrams showing how to place the eye relative to the prism, and the arrangements for drawing natural size, reducing, enlarging, correcting photographs, reversed drawing and anamorphosis. There are two copies of the Lechertier Barbe leaflet, with and without a Monomark address which, we understand, places them one each side of the mid 1930s; the firm left Jermyn Street about 1979. A camera lucida at the Science Museum is exactly similar to the illustrations; it is particularly distinguished by a rack-and-pinion movement in the draw stem next to the prism. The clamp bears the full name and address of Lechertier Barbe with a small 'PB' in an oval frame.

Vignettes from the price list of P Berville, Paris, showing a camera lucida in use. Left: copying a drawing or a photograph. Centre: sketching a landscape. Right: drawing a portrait.

We are reasonably confident that the instrument was made by Berville and that Lechertier Barbe were the sole importers. The prism is a right-angle prism silvered on the hypotenuse; when lying horizontally, with the hypotenuse as a base, the image is upright and correct. The image is inverted when the prism is tilted forward, thus a picture placed upside down would be copied right way up but reversed, exactly the requirement for making a printing block.

Stanley's book was reprinted in 1925 with the same text and illustrations as in the 1888 edition.[19] An undated edition of Harmsworth described and illustrated Wollaston's prism with a reference to Dr Hooke.[20] Hutchinson printed the Wollaston illustration from Stanley's book with a title and a brief, though enigmatic, explanation.[21]

1940–60

This period of war and recovery has, perhaps not surprisingly, provided very few references to the camera lucida. Gernsheim (1955) made it quite clear that it 'is *not* a camera at all . . .' and 'It will be evident that there is no connection between this instrument and Dr. Hooke's camera lucida. . . .'[22]

Nedoluha in his paper on the cultural history of technical drawing refers only to Wollaston with an illustration of the prism and the camera lucida being used by an artist in the field.[23] *Newnes' Practical Mechanics* published an article on the 'Camera Obscura with Details of the Camera Lucida'.[24]

Chambers's Encyclopaedia described Wollaston's prism with a clear diagram.[25] The *Encyclopaedia Britannica* devoted a considerable amount of space to the instrument with diagrams of a simple camera lucida and of Wollaston's prism.[26] It is delightfully vague over the date, 'About the beginning of the 19th century Dr. Wollaston invented . . .'. Although it said that the camera lucida '. . . was of considerable importance to draughtsmen' and that 'It was largely used for copying, for reducing or for enlarging existing drawings', there is no mention of its use by artists. This may be a reflection of the use in America where the photographic camera made a very strong impact on amateur artists.

1960–85

Wollaston's prism remains the standard instrument described in encyclopaedias and dictionaries today but it is Alexander's Graphic Mirror design which was available in this period, albeit as children's toys or for do-it-yourself enthusiasts (see pp. 46–8).

We have one undated page from an unknown American catalogue, illustrating a camera lucida which appears to be the same as on the Berville leaflet. The instrument was supplied with twelve lenses and the price was $105. The Berville camera lucida was priced at 325 francs.

Encyclopaedia Britannica describes Wollaston's prism with a diagram, the necessity for lenses and the difficulties encountered when using the instrument are explained.[27] Unfortunately the description of the Abbé camera lucida for use with the microscope is incorrect.

During a visit to Canada one of us (JHH) learnt that camera lucidas are still used in museum and university research departments. It is not unkind to mention that the users are, in the main, of an older generation and the camera lucidas even older! A collector described over the telephone a camera lucida inscribed 'Charles Gaginni, Paris' which appeared to have a Wollaston prism. We have gained the impression that camera lucidas were, up to about 1960, an everyday tool in drawing offices in Canada and America whereas in England the camera lucida was more of an artist's aid for both amateurs and professionals.

The last two decades have been an era of the decorative 'coffee table' book which serves the excellent use of providing illustrations, usually of very good quality. One such book illustrated a camera lucida made by Bancks and another by Bate.[28]

During 1984 the Edinburgh City Council produced at Calton Hill Observatory a 'Television Panorama of Edinburgh' which was mistakenly called a '20th century camera lucida'.

This survey shows that Wollaston's patent, the four-sided prism, has consistently been the definition, in fact and principle, of the camera lucida; and no doubt it will remain so. Nevertheless, in spite of the ingenious alternative designs of Amici, Govi and Nachet, Alexander's Graphic Mirror of the 1830s, the invention of a relatively obscure optician in Exeter, remains the most simple, practical and easy-to-use camera lucida.

References

1. *Notes and Queries* 1853 **8** 271, 503
2. Marbach O 1850 *Physikalisches Lexikon*
3. Douglas J C 1880 Use of silver films in improved instruments of the camera lucida class *Proceedings of the Asiatic Society of Bengal* 73–6 Pl. 1
4. *The American Cyclopaedia* 1860 p. 307
5. *Chambers's Encyclopaedia* 1874 pp. 563–7
6. Knight E H 1877 *Practical Dictionary of Mechanics* p. 434
7. *Encyclopaedia of Photography* 1879 (reprint 1947) (New York: Arno) p. 74
8. Privat-Deschanel and Focillon Ad 1864 *Dictionnaire Generale des Sciences Theoriques et Applique* p. 438
9. *Encyclopaedia Britannica* 1875–89 740–1 Pl. 34
10. *Century Dictionary* 1889 p. 777
11. *English Cyclopaedia* 1891 pp. 532–3
12. Ogilvie J and Annandale 1898 *Imperial Dictionary of the English Language*
13. Vincent B 1889 *Haydn's Dictionary of Dates* p. 159
14. Feldhaus F M 1914 *Die Technik* p. 549
15. *Harmsworth's Encyclopaedia* 1906 p. 446
16. *Encyclopaedia Britannica* 1910 p. 104

17. Berville P *Price List* nd. Royal Ontario Museum, Toronto
18. Lechertier Barbe *Two Price Lists* nd. Science Museum, South Kensington, London
19. Stanley W F 1925 *Mathematical, Drawing and Measuring Instruments* p. 143
20. *Harmsworth's Encyclopaedia* 8 vol. edn nd. 1920?
21. Hutchinson W 1935 *1001 Wonderful Things* (London: Hutchinson)
22. Gernsheim H 1955 *History of Photography* (Oxford: Oxford University Press) p. 19
23. Nedoluha A 1959 Kultergeschichte des technischen Zeichens *Blatter fur Technikgeschichte* **21** 129
24. The camera obscura *Newnes' Practical Mechanics* March 1955 259
25. *Chambers's Encyclopaedia* 1950 p. 813
26. *Encyclopaedia Britannica* 1957 pp. 657–8
27. *Encyclopaedia Britannica* 1973 p. 700
28. Wynter H and Turner A 1975 *Scientific Instruments* (Studio Vista) pp. 226–7

The Graphic Telescope

Few people have had the good fortune, as did Cornelius Varley, to possess the attributes and skills of a scientist, artist and instrument maker. He was the second son of a family of three boys and two girls and was born at Hackney, London, on 21 November 1781. Their father, Richard Varley, was a Lincolnshire man who had lived with his first wife in Yorkshire but, on her death, he went to London and married a Miss Fleetwood. Although their father was averse to the arts all three boys became artists, while one of the girls married William Mulready, a painter who designed the first penny post envelope in 1840.

Cornelius was only ten years old when his father died, at which time his mother had three younger children. Mrs Varley moved her family to a smaller house in an obscure court opposite St Luke's Hospital, Old Street, London. She was sympathetic towards the arts and allowed John, the eldest boy, to follow his natural ability and desire to be an artist; he had previously been apprenticed to a silversmith. Cornelius was adopted and apprenticed by his uncle Samuel Varley, a watchmaker, jeweller and instrument maker, who had considerable scientific interests. Soon after taking Cornelius, about 1794, Samuel Varley started to give scientific lectures. He conducted chemical experiments and founded the Chemical and Philosophical Society which was the forerunner of the Royal Institution. Cornelius stayed with his uncle throughout his teens; it was during this period that his interest in science and his skill as a mechanic were nurtured. However, he also continued the childhood companion-

Cornelius Varley. This portrait accompanied an obituary notice in the *Illustrated London News* 25 October 1873. It was '. . . engraved from a photograph by Messrs Varley Brothers, Oakley-street, Chelsea'.

ship with his brother John, accompanying him on sketching and painting walks in and around London.

About 1800, when he was 20 years of age, Cornelius decided to study art full-time, so he left his uncle and went to live with his brother John. They both attended Dr Monro's evenings in Adelphi Terrace where they met a group of young artists, which included Turner and Cotman, under the Doctor's patronage. Cornelius became a proficient and enthusiastic artist receiving commissions and teaching. He was one of the founder members of the Water-Colour Society in 1804 and became a regular contributor to the exhibitions of that Society and the Royal Academy. In spite of this intense activity in the arts Cornelius maintained his scientific interests, particularly in optics and microscopy. He joined the Society of Arts and took an active part in the work of that body throughout his life, besides contributing articles to the *Transactions*. He also had papers published in the *Microscopical Society Journal*. Cornelius Varley died on 2 October 1873, at almost 93 years of age.

The Society of Arts obituary notice was surprisingly brief in view of his work for the Society and that for a number of years he made the drawings for the illustrations in the *Transactions*.[1] The *Illustrated London News* printed a portrait and a considerable account of Varley's achievements.[2] In January of the following year, 1874, the *Journal of the Society of Arts* printed a small notice from the Committee of the Society in which 'it was resolved to recommend that a memoir of the late Cornelius Varley, illustrated with a photographic portrait, should be prepared and issued . . . and a copy presented to his family, in token of the high estimation in which he was held. . . .'[3] A search of the

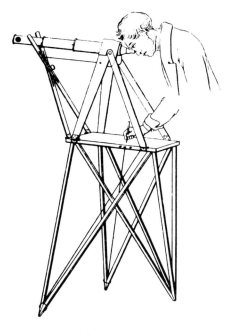

Drawn by C. Varley.

Varley's Patent Graphic Telescope complete with a drawing-table stand.

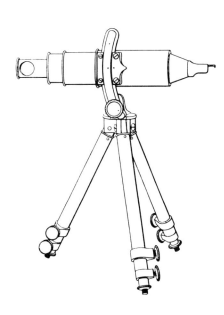

Journal for the following ten years brought no evidence of a memoir.

Varley's scientific pursuits ranged over a wide field. He designed an artist's easel, made observations on the sap of water plants, and collaborated with Andrew Pritchard, his nephew and apprentice, on making the first diamond lens. He also made improvements to lens grinding machinery and invented the Graphic Telescope, for which he obtained a Patent No 3430 in 1811.[4]

The Patent Graphic Telescope (PGT) designed by Cornelius Varley consisted essentially of a low-power astronomical telescope with a mirror at each end, which effectively made it a camera lucida. Astronomical telescopes are non-erecting, that is the image is upside down and reversed. The vertical mirror in front of the Graphic Telescope is at 45° to the axis of the telescope to correct the image left-to-right. Thus the telescope does not point directly at the view but is at right angles to it. At the eyepiece the mirror is at 45° with the horizontal to correct the inverted image. The upper edge of this mirror is ground away to a sharp edge, so that when looking down into the mirror the artist sees the telescopic image of the object or scenery and by looking over the edge of the mirror sees the paper below. The principle is exactly the same as Wollaston's prism, a split-pupil camera lucida, and an eyeshade with a small hole was provided. And, as with the prism, it was necessary to match the image from the telescope to the distance of the paper and pencil from the eyepiece mirror. This was achieved very simply by a slight in or out movement of the eyepiece. Thus for any given magnification of the telescope it was possible to make small or large sketches merely by having the drawing paper near or far from the eyepiece. However, when making very small drawings such as vignettes or miniatures the eyepiece adjustment was not sufficient. Varley

A short model of the Graphic Telescope with quadrant mount which retained a constant eyepiece-to-paper distance whenever the angle of the telescope was changed.

Varley's Graphic Microscope. From *The Magazine of Science and School of Arts* (1840).

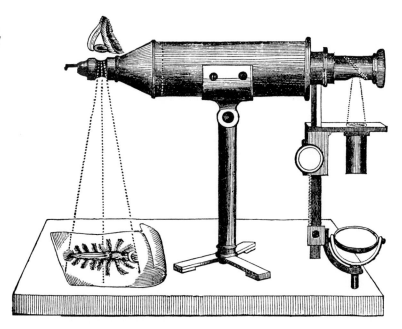

said he then used a spectacle lens (a biconvex lens) '. . . the focus of which is so short as to let me see the paper when placed so near as to reduce the image to the required size'.

Ray diagram of Varley's Graphic Microscope. Redrawn from Varley, Cornelius 1836 Graphic Telescope *Transactions of the Society for the Encouragement of Arts, Manufactures and Commerce* (now the Royal Society of Arts).

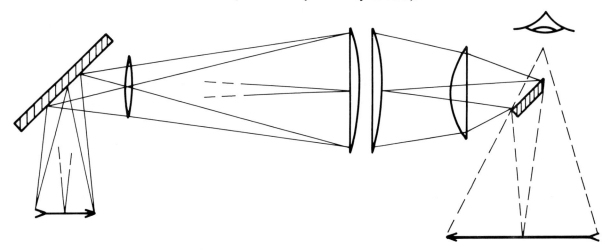

Although the telescope was nominally of low power
it was possible to alter the magnification by changing
the eyepiece and possibly the object glass. We are
uncertain about exactly how many eyepieces were included, and whether a second object glass was supplied
with each instrument. The Science Museum, South
Kensington, has four Graphic Telescopes though none
is complete. One is convertible to a Graphic Microscope, it is said to have been Varley's because 'C.
Varley's own inst.' is scratched on the dovetail slot.
The most interesting model is numbered 37. The body
is a mahogany tube and there are two object glasses.
The object glass mirror is at the eyepiece end of the
tube and the telescope was constructed without a field
lens. We believe it to have been an experimental model,
but the number 37 is an enigma.

Among the Varley papers at the Whipple Museum of
the History of Science, Cambridge, there is a small
piece of paper, heavily pockmarked and unsuitable for
reproduction with the following handwritten table:

	Powers of the Graphic Telescope with		
	first	second or	third eyepieces
small object glass	4	6	
large object glass	$8\frac{1}{2}$	12	20

Varley described how to convert the Graphic Telescope so that it may be used as a low-power microscope
for drawing, this involved a short-focus object glass.
He also designed a separate instrument, the Graphic
Microscope, which he said was '. . . as far as artists
require.'[5]

Unlike Wollaston who published the 'Description' of
his camera lucida within months of receiving the
Patent, Varley described his Graphic Telescope in the
*Transactions of the Society for the Encouragement of
Arts, Manufacturing and Commerce* some 25 years after
receiving the Patent, by which time the patent rights

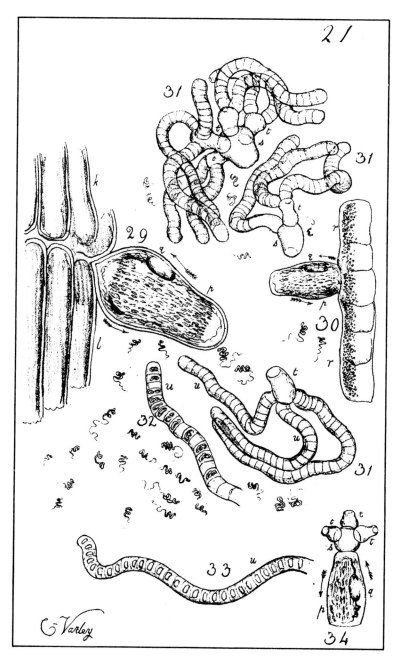

Cornelius Varley used his Graphic Microscope when making this drawing for his paper 'On *Chara vulgaris*' one of a group of green algae commonly known as stoneworts. From *The Transactions of the Microscopical Society* (1849). The paper was read to the Society in 1845.

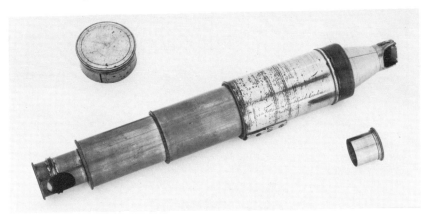

Cornelius Varley's own Graphic Telescope which is now at the Science Museum, South Kensington, London.

had long expired.[5] Four years later, in 1840, the popular *Magazine of Science and School of Arts* published an article entitled 'Varley's Graphic Microscope and Telescope', much of which was taken directly from the *Transactions*.[6]

In the introduction to his description Varley explained that several adjustments and improvements had been made since the original patent. He had also designed three sorts of stands; one of these was a complete telescope support and drawing table, another was a tubular tripod similar to a photographic tripod. To this tripod he added a tilting device in the form of a segment of a circle centred on the telescope eyepiece, so that the distance of the eyepiece to the drawing paper remained constant whatever tilt was put on the telescope.

In her book on Hanoverian instrument makers E G R Taylor wrote, 'Varley is described as an amateur optician, an artist and inventor.'[7] The designation 'amateur' may have some truth, though Varley was never a dilettante. Our researches have not shown him to have been generally 'in trade' as an instrument maker. There is little doubt that he had a workshop but it may have been only for making lenses; we have

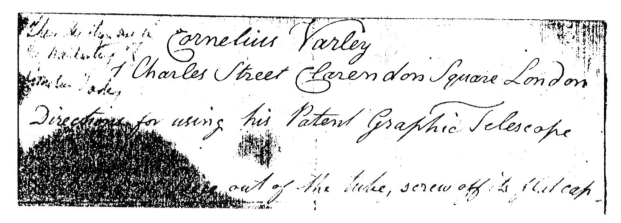

Part of Varley's manuscript draft for the 'Directions for using the Patent Graphic Telescope'.

Andrew Pritchard's account of this activity.[8] It is possible that Varley contracted out all the mechanical work. We have no evidence for this supposition apart from the style and manner of Varley's description, of him gradually improving and building up the graphic telescope and microscope, and that the graphic telescopes at the science museums of London, Oxford and Cambridge are not numbered, other than the curious mahogany model mentioned above. These factors suggest the attitude of the dedicated amateur. In the Patent Varley is described as 'Artist'.

The Whipple Museum, Cambridge, has a manuscript draft of instructions for the Graphic Telescope written by Varley.[9] At the Science Museum, South Kensington, there is an expanded printed version of the draft which may be a printer's proof because it is corrected with deletions and additions which appear to be in the same hand as the Whipple manuscript.[10] The printed version says that the Graphic Telescope was 'invented by Cornelius Varley and sold by him at', followed by the address in manuscript '1, Charles Street, Clarendon Square, Somers Town' after which 'London' is printed. Unfortunately neither document is dated.

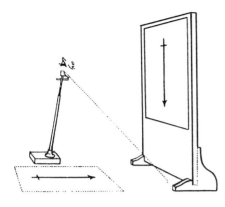

A simple camera lucida of the split-pupil type. The artist had to look partially at the pencil whilst observing the reflected view. This type of camera lucida may have been used by a printer's artist for copying directly onto a lithographic stone. From Varley, Cornelius 1845 *A Treatise on Optical Drawing Instruments.*

Varley closed his description of the Graphic Telescope with a note on the advantages of the instrument. Some of these are equally applicable to any other camera lucida but he does have a point when he says 'Wild or savage animals may be sketched from a place of safety, at such a distance as not to rouse or disturb them; also timid animals, which will not remain still if we go too near them!' It may be that as a result of his illustrative work for the Society of Arts *Transactions* that Varley mentioned, '. . . by taking away the object-speculum [mirror], these objects or views may be drawn at once on stone the reverse way, and so be printed the right way; thus we may now publish real sketches from nature'. In his Patent Specification of 1811, the phrase 'on stone' was qualified by 'in the German mode of printing' which reminds us that lithography had only recently been invented by Senefelder in 1798. The final project in Varley's description is indeed venturesome, 'If this telescope, table and draughtsman, were mounted on a polar axis (a strong axis placed parallel to that of the earth), and moved by a clock, a most perfect map of the stars could be traced, of any required size; for he would then direct his telescope to succeeding portions, as though they were all quite stationary.'

Perhaps the Graphic Telescope was most useful for portraiture, the low-power telescope enabling the artist to make a life-size drawing without having to approach the sitter too closely. The landscape artist sometimes sees a pictorial composition in a distant scene; the Graphic Telescope would allow the artist to sketch the distant detail and maintain the shallow perspective. The British Museum Print Room has a number of sketches and portraits drawn by Cornelius Varley with the aid of his instrument and it is known that his brother John also used the telescope. John Sell Cotman may have used it when sketching in Normandy, but there is some doubt about this which will be dealt with later.

Varley's instrument was the only one of its kind but it does not appear to have been a commercial success. It is thought that he made the Patent Graphic Telescope at the request of acquaintances to whom he gave personal tuition. Our evidence for this is the lack of commercial material and the rarity of existing instruments.

The Patent Graphic Telescope was expensive, heavy and cumbersome, and as a camera lucida it was just as difficult to use as Wollaston's prism, or any other split-pupil type of instrument. Furthermore, the prism or any camera lucida could be used with any telescope. It was advantageous to use a low-power telescope which, curiously, was the subject of a patent within a few weeks of Varley's own patent. Dr David Brewster and William Harris designed the Micrometrical Telescope, Patent No 3453 (1811) for measuring angles and distances.[11] It was possible to alter the magnification of the telescope without changing the lenses and it was very suitable for use with a camera lucida. Both the Edinburgh and London *Encyclopaedias* referred to the Micrometrical Telescope in their articles on the camera lucida but made no mention of Varley's Graphic Telescope.

It is interesting to note that Wollaston in his 'Description' did not mention the possibility of using the prism with either a telescope or microscope. It may be that he was not concerned with the application of his invention, or he was not interested in drawing or art generally. In 1823 Wollaston received a note from a Mr George Coventry of Wandsworth Common, enquiring about the use of a camera lucida with a telescope. Wollaston's reply was helpful and included a sketch of

23/B3   no. 53.
Monday 25 Aug^L
1823

Sir
      After two months absence from home I have just received your letter & in reply have merely to say that objects so distant as not to be seen without a telescope may be drawn by means of it —.

      The window here sketched is full 900 yards distant from my house & was drawn by

Part of Wollaston's letter to George Coventry, dated Monday 25 August 1823.

a man at a window some 900 yards distant. However, the sketch is no credit to a camera lucida—it might have been made freehand with the aid of a telescope.

The first reference we have for the application of a camera lucida to a telescope is from the instrument maker R B Bate, in 1809, some two years after Wollaston's 'Description'.[12] Bate mentioned the use of a camera lucida with a microscope and continued, 'A telescope may likewise be employed . . . the face of the prism must be brought into contact with the eye glass . . . a distant object is then approximated . . . and may be delineated in a manner at once pleasing, novel, and correct.' W G Horner wrote in 1815 in praise of Dr Wollaston's 'numerous inventions' and continued, 'These remarks are eminently appropriate to the Camera Lucida. As a corrective of the erroneous decisions of the eye, or a succidaneum to the labour of educating that organ, the utility of the beautiful little machine is well known . . . but I am ignorant if any philosopher has been struck with the still more extensive uses to which it may be adapted in combination with the microscope and telescope . . . The astronomer, and even the military officer . . . would derive important assistance from the use of the *graphic telescope*.'[13] The expression 'graphic telescope' (Horner's italics) is a salutary reminder of the isolation and paucity of communication during the early part of the last century —Horner was writing from Bath! It also confirms Cornelius Varley's reticence and what we believe to be his somewhat non-commercial attitude.

The *Encyclopaedia Britannica Supplement* of 1824 also mentioned fixing Wollaston's camera lucida to a telescope, the power of which should be small.[14] However, it also said that 'A plain reflecting glass, fixed at an angle of 45° . . . will also give an image . . . so situated that [it] may be traced with a pencil. Varley's patent graphic telescope is upon this principle.' The *Edinburgh Encyclopaedia* of 1830 set out the procedure for sketching a panorama by means of a camera lucida on a telescope, '. . . and even when the place of the observer is embosomed in an amphitheatre of mountains which rise around him with various elevations, the field of view may be enlarged by diminishing the power of the telescope'.[15] The article continued by recommending Dr Brewster's micrometrical telescope as being, 'particularly applicable'. Varley's Graphic Telescope was not mentioned. This account is an interesting example of editorial copying or sharing of information, for the wording is almost identical with the 'Camera lucida' article in the *London Encyclopaedia* of 1829.[16]

Perhaps the most interesting paper on the use of a camera lucida and a telescope for sketching panoramas is by Professor C F Zantedeschi (1869).[17] He referred to Francesco Carlini, Director of the Astronomical Observatory at Milan, who in the year 1818 or 1819 placed a Wollaston prism on his telescope in order to draw a panorama of the mountains surrounding his observatory. Apparently Carlini did not complete the drawing, but had he done so it would have been about 20 metres wide. Zantedeschi said that an optician, Carlo Ponti, also used a prism on a telescope. He also referred to a newly invented instrument called a 'Tele-iconograph' by a Paris instrument maker M Revoil. However, Zantedeschi reported that it was nothing more than Wollaston's camera lucida applied to a terrestrial telescope mounted on a stand in the style of a theodolite.

About 1820 Thomas Hornor, a Yorkshire land-surveyor, conceived the project of painting a panorama of London. At that time the ball and cross on top of St Paul's were being repaired and Hornor successfully applied for an observatory hut to be built amidst the scaffolding above the cross. From this vantage point he produced some 280 sketches which, between the years 1825 and 1830, were translated into one of the largest ever panorama paintings. The Colosseum, designed by Decimus Burton, was erected in Regent's Park specially for the panorama. In order to make the prelimi-

This engraving is the only known illustration showing any detail of Thomas Hornor's apparatus.

nary sketches Hornor employed an apparatus; but exactly what that consisted of we have no clear evidence. Like many another craftsman–entrepreneur of the last century Hornor was extremely secretive about his method, though otherwise he was a flamboyant showman. In one of his two pamphlets he said he had, '...constructed an apparatus by which the most distant and intricate scenery may be delineated with mathematical accuracy...'. A small engraving frontispiece

The 'Vale of Neath' by Thomas Hornor. This painting shows the artist with his apparatus and a picnic party—note the wine bottles cooling in the pond! The picture, a water-colour, measures 21.5 × 14.5 cm ($8\frac{1}{2}$ × $5\frac{3}{4}$ inches).

to this pamphlet shows what may be a telescope on a theodolite-type mounting. In one of his water-colour paintings he shows a piece of apparatus which is highly improbable. It appears to be a large-diameter tube on a stand throwing rays of light towards a white sheet hung over the bough of a tree, in full daylight without any shading over the screen area.

The literature on Thomas Hornor was searched and out of ten notices of him and the panorama of London seven said he used a Graphic Telescope; one, telescopes and machinery; one, a camera lucida on a telescope; and one did not refer to any apparatus. Ralph

Hyde mentioned a camera lucida in his 1977 paper on Hornor but this was modified in his 1982 book on the Colosseum as the result of discussion with the present authors.[18,19]

R D Altick in his book 'The Shows of London' reproduces an illustration from Hornor's 'Prospectus' which shows the scaffolding and observatory hut above the cross on St Paul's.[20]

Appendix: Thomas Hornor

For his panorama of London, Thomas Hornor had the financial backing of a banker, Rowland Stephenson, who absconded in December 1828. The mounting debts caused Hornor to flee to America in the following year. There he died in 1844, apparently insane. The painting of the panorama was completed about 1830 by E T Parris and a team of fellow artists.

The following extracts refer to the apparatus employed by Hornor when making his first sketches. It is quite likely that authors writing after 1873 copied the obituary notice of Cornelius Varley in the *Illustrated London News* of that year.

1813 Hornor T *Description of an Improved Method of Delineating Estates* (p. 8)

'That a plan may be drawn up with the same mathematical precision, and afterwards so finished as to form a faithful and interesting picture of the various features of the property, comprehending the prospects which it commands, as if beheld in a camera obscura or from a lofty eminence, has been proved by the enlarged specimens which I have recently submitted to public inspection.'

The instrument is not mentioned but is shown in a cartouche, the frontispiece engraving.

1819 Hornor T *Album of Water-Colour Paintings of the Vale of Neath* (at the British Museum Print Room). No 23 'Vale of Neath from Bon Main' (mis-spelling of Bwa Maen)

This painting shows a group of people, with Hornor, beside a piece of apparatus. It appears to be a large tube with rays of light issuing from it towards a white sheet hung over the bough of a tree. It is clearly intended to portray projection, but it is all in full daylight and there is no shrouding or any attempt to shade the projection area. As it appears in the painting the apparatus and situation are impracticable. The following is from Hornor's legend to the painting. 'The prospect of the Vale from the summit of Bow Main is so fine in its composition that I bestowed a little labour in erecting a screen from the weather, and had made such progress in tracing the objects before me when a blast of wind scattered my humble efforts, house and apparatus into the woods below.'

1823 Intelligence relative to the Fine Arts. Mr. Hornor's view of London from above St. Paul's *European Magazine* (June) p. 541.

'. . . in a chamber suspended from the highest of these supports, occupied in the complicated and difficult task of a mathematical survey of the wide-spread and multitudinously peopled capital of the British monarchy.'

The instrument is not mentioned.

1823 Hornor T Prospectus *View of London* p. 13 (Hornor wrote in the third person)

'In the course of his professional studies, he constructed an apparatus by which the most distant and intricate scenery may be delineated with mathematical accuracy; and this machinery he was desirous of applying to the execution of a work for which he considered himself so amply prepared.'

1828 Elmes, James *Metropolitan Improvements or London in the Nineteenth Century* p. 68

'In taking the views, Mr. Hornor was aided by his topographical knowledge of the country as a skilful land-surveyor, by powerful telescopes and by curious machinery, for executing his sketches.

1823 Natural Philosophy *Library of Useful Knowledge* vol. 2 p. 26

A footnote concerning Varley using his Patent Graphic

Telescope in Wales and at Newstead Abbey, the final sentence said: 'We have been informed that this instrument was the one employed in making the panoramic view of the metropolis from the top of St. Paul's, for the exhibition of which a building in the Regent's Park, called the Coliseum, has recently been erected.'

1853 Drawing instruments *Journal of the Society of Arts* p. 538

'Mr. Hornor, by means of the Graphic Telescope, produced one of the largest panoramas ever painted,— London as seen from the top of St. Paul's,—a task almost hopeless without such aid.'

1863 *London Review of Politics, Society, Literature, Art and Science* (Aug. 22) p. 211

'... he did not make the pictorial effect that gave him the key to the banker's purse, for the camera-lucida sketches Mr. Hornor took were transmitted by him to some eminent members of the Old Water-Colour Society, and were elaborated by them into exquisite drawings... Everything was superlative with the Yorkshire surveyor; even the camera-lucida he sketched with must be like that of no other man, and he had it specially adapted by Carey [Cary] to a telescope.'

1873 Obituary, Cornelius Varley *Illustrated London News* (25 October)

'The large panorama of London, exhibited for some time at the Colosseum, was sketched by the aid of the graphic telescope from the gallery of St. Paul's.'

1891 Roget J L *History of the Old Water-Colour Society* p. 408

'It (Varley's graphic telescope) was employed by Hornor in making his sketches from the top of St. Paul's, for the panorama of London exhibited at the Colosseum.'

1892 Story A T *Life of John Linnell* vol. 2 p. 222

'His [Cornelius Varley] invention of the Graphic Telescope has already been referred to. The Colosseum it would appear, owed its origin to this instrument. Mr. T. Hornor, after satisfying himself of its capabilities, having erected an observatory on the dome of St. Paul's, where he fitted up a Graphic Telescope, and traced his magnificent panorama of London for the reception of which the Colosseum in Regent's Park was built.'

1899 Cornelius Varley *Dictionary of National Biography*
'He invented the Graphic telescope . . . which was used by T. Hornor in laying down his great panorama of London for the Coliseum in Regent's Park . . .'.

1902 Nelson E M, Waddel's erecting microscope *Journal of the Royal Microscopical Society* p. 291
'It was by one of these instruments (the 'Graphic Telescope') that the sketch of London was made from the top of St. Paul's for the panorama exhibited at the Colosseum, which probably some of us may remember.'

The following passages are from: Jenkins, Elis 1971, Thomas Hornor *Stewart William's Glamorgan Historian* 7 (Cowbridge: Brown)

[p. 38] 'He does not reveal what his apparatus is, but from a water-colour he made of the Vale of Neath from Bwa Maen, and from one of the emblems in the cartouche at the end of his little book, we may guess that it included either some form of camera lucida . . . or one of the many forms of camera obscura. The Bwa Maen picnic scene shows the artist holding what looks like a fat telescope with a large enough aperture to project an inverted image[†] of a landscape even in daylight.'

[p. 42] 'The viewpoint is on the mountain side a little north-east of Resolven, and as one would expect of a landscape produced by the lenses of Hornor's Contraption there is severe foreshortening of the perspective to the left and to the right of the picture; but the distortion is not unpleasing.'

[p. 44] 'Anyone familiar with the natural features depicted, many of which cannot have changed much since 1815, will see that despite his much-advertised Contraption he can slice in half the anticlinal fold of Bwa Maen (the Stone Bow), completely miss the lateral migration of Scwd Gwladys—both familiar features to schoolboy geologists—make the Mellte flow upstream at Porth-yr-Ogof,

[†]There is not an image on the screen in the painting.

place the sun in the North at Ynysgerwn and achieve an unreal perspective in his Pontypridd Bridge. Unless one insists on photographic realism, these slips of the pencil need not be disturbing; indeed, in some of the drawings the Contraption has done its work too effectively, so that the picture reproduced the scene almost as the composite visual impression of a group of onlookers, a kind of artistic identikit.'

References

Biographical information on Cornelius Varley may be found in:

Bryan M 1895 *Dictionary of Painters and Engravers*
The Connoisseur (1943)
Dictionary of National Biography (1899)
Encyclopaedia Britannica (1910)
Hardie M 1967 *Water-Colour Painting in Britain*
Illustrated London News (1873)
Redgrave S 1874 *Dictionary of Artists of the English School*
Roget J L 1891 *History of the Old Water-Colour Society*
Royal Academy Catalogue 1972 *English Drawings and Water-Colours 1550–1850 in the collection of Mr. & Mrs. Paul Mellon* (London: Royal Academy of Arts)
Journal of the Society of Arts (1873)

1. *Journal of the Society of Arts* 1873 Obituary, Cornelius Varley **21** 881
2. *Illustrated London News* 1873 The late Mr. Cornelius Varley **63** 389
3. *Journal of the Society of Arts* 1874 Varley Testimonial **22** 133
4. Varley, Cornelius 1811 A new construction of a telescope or optical instrument for viewing distant objects, & for other useful purposes, with a suitable table or stand for the same *British Patent* No 3430
5. Varley C 1836 Graphic telescope *Transactions of the Society for the Encouragement of Arts, Manufactures and Commerce* **50** 120–39
6. *Magazine of Science and School of Arts* 1840 Varley's Graphic Microscope and Telescope **2** 218–20
7. Taylor E G R 1960 *The Mathematical Practitioners of Hanoverian England, 1714–1840* (Cambridge: Cambridge University Press/Institute of Navigation) p. 377

8. Pritchard A 1827 On the art of forming diamonds into single lenses for microscopes *Quarterly Journal of Science, Literature and Art* (July–Dec.) 15–21

9. Cornelius Varley. Directions for using his Patent Graphic Telescope. Inventory no C3:12,13 *Manuscript* Whipple Museum of the History of Science, Cambridge

10. Varley C Directions for using the Patent Graphic Telescope. Inventory no 1891–12. Science Museum, South Kensington, London

11. Brewster D and Harris H 1811 Certain optical instruments for measuring angles, and also certain improvements upon and additions to telescopes and other optical instruments, for the purpose of measuring angles and distances with facility, and other purposes *British Patent* No 3453

12. Bate R B 1809 On the camera lucida. letter *Journal of Natural Philosophy, Chemistry and the Arts* **24** 146–50

13. Horner W G 1815 New and important combinations with the camera lucida *Annals of Philosophy* **6** 281–3

14. *Encyclopaedia Britannica Supplement* 1823–4 pp. 587–8 Pl. 46

15. *Edinburgh Encyclopaedia* 1830 pp. 297–9 Pl. 109

16. *London Encyclopaedia* 1829 pp. 67–9 Pl.

17. Zantedeschi C F 1869–70 Della camera lucida di Wollaston *Atti del Istituto Veneto di Scienze* **15** 1065–7

18. Hyde, Ralph 1977 Thomas Hornor: pictural land surveyor *Imago Mundi* **29** 23–34

19. Hyde, Ralph 1982 *The Regent's Park Colosseum* (London: Ackermann)

20. Altick R D 1978 *The Shows of London* (Cambridge, MA: Harvard University Press) pp. 141–50

Drawing with a Camera Lucida

The rediscovery of perspective in the thirteenth and fourteenth centuries brought about both the mathematical theory for the illusion of depth in pictures and a variety of drawing aids or perspective machines for the precise sketching of objects and scenery. Many of the machines consisted merely of a framed grid or a sheet of glass, whilst others had a system of levers similar to a pantograph. Whatever the mechanism, they all incorporated a sight system whereby the artist traced the outline of an object or scene with a pointer attached to a pencil. All such drawing aids, including the camera obscura and camera lucida, are referred to as optical drawing instruments. It may be said that the camera lucida is the most recent drawing aid and it is quite likely that it will be the last. The camera obscura is still in use in design offices and there may be the occasional revival of an early device such as a framed grid which was on the market for a brief period about ten years ago.[1]

A considerable amount of confusion still surrounds the camera obscura and the camera lucida. Wollaston compared the two instrumens in the 'Description' (see p. 10), but we may briefly take another assessment. The camera obscura is bulky, as an artist's aid it can vary in size from that of a shoe box to that of a wigwam tent containing a small table. In contrast, the camera lucida is small enough to be carried in a pocket or handbag. A lens and mirror are essential components of a camera obscura, producing a real image of the landscape simi-

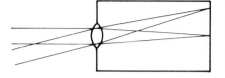

The camera obscura. Rays of light from a scene are brought to focus by a lens, creating a real image which may be traced. The camera obscura was adapted for photography (1839) whereby the real image acts upon a sensitive film to make a negative or transparency.

lar to the picture made by a slide projector. An artist is able to observe and trace the image with complete freedom of the head and eyes.

When sketching with a box camera obscura the image is transmitted through a sheet of tracing paper and is consequently somewhat feeble. Although a hood was fitted around the drawing area to shield off extraneous light the artist, when working out of doors, usually chose a shaded spot under a tree. This was advantageous to ladies of the eighteenth and nineteenth centuries for whom a sunburnt complexion was thought to be coarse and vulgar.

The camera lucida presents only a reflection of a scene, there is nothing to be seen when looking directly at the drawing paper. The artist must observe the reflection and the pencil at one and the same time with one eye held steadfastly in a fixed position. When using the camera lucida it is important to obtain a nice balance between the light on the drawing paper and the brilliance of the reflected scene. This requirement frequently inhibited the use of sunhats and parasols, which cast a shadow over the drawing paper.

The view in a camera obscura is limited to about 35° by the focal length of the lens and the size of the drawing area, whereas the angle of view with a camera lucida may be as much as 70° and the size of the drawing may be varied. The 70° angle of view mentioned by Wollaston, and frequently quoted, is in fact somewhat misleading. It may be achieved by a slight rotation of the prism but at the same time the balance of lighting is usually upset.

Art historians frequently suggest that distortion in pictures results from the artist's use of a drawing aid.

A

B

A: a reflex camera obscura. An image of a scene is made by the lens and is reflected from a mirror to a sheet of thin translucent paper resting on a clear glass. This type of camera obscura usually measured $20 \times 25 \times 35$ cm ($8 \times 10 \times 14$ inches). In the eighteenth century it was extremely popular as a sketching aid.

B: a camera lucida. By carefully placing the eye over the edge of the prism the artist sees a reflection of the scene and the drawing paper together. There is no image on the paper as in the camera obscura. The prism is very small, approximately $1 \times 1 \times 2$ cm $\frac{3}{8} \times \frac{3}{8} \times \frac{3}{4}$ inches). The supporting rod may be adjusted in height, usually from 20 to 35 cm (8 to 14 inches).

Certainly a lens in any instrument will introduce distortion which may be noticeable around the edges of a picture. Many artists were aware of this failing in the camera obscura and used it only for sketching the central detail of a scene. However, the same problem arose when drawing landscapes with a camera lucida. A lens had to be introduced in order to make both the scene and the pencil and paper appear to be the same distance from the eye. The historians also refer to line quality and steep perspective as evidence of the use of a drawing aid, for example a firm continuous line indicating a traced image as opposed to the tentative feathery line of a sketch by eye. However, we feel these to be somewhat tenuous pointers.

Of all the drawing aids the camera lucida was, perhaps, the least cumbersome to use, but there is little doubt that it was the most difficult to master. It required that very human acquisition 'a knack', and a good deal of perseverence and practice. These remarks apply only to the split-pupil type of camera lucida of which, as we have discovered, Wollaston's prism was the most prevalent. Regrettably little is known of the extent to which the see-through camera lucidas such as Alexander's Graphic Mirror were bought and used by amateur and professional artists. A booklist of about 1838 from the print dealer Ackermann advertises 'New Drawing Books' and 'The Graphic Mirror, an improved and portable instrument for sketching in true perspective... The difficulties known to exist in the Camera Lucida are entirely obviated in this instrument.'

Advice on drawing technique with the camera lucida was sparse. Only four encyclopaedias offered any help and that was confined to it being 'by no means easy', and requiring 'considerable practice'. When compared with the results from an experienced draughtsman 'the camera lucida is laid aside as soon as it is taken in hand, as much practice is essential to its useful application'. Hardly encouraging words for one hoping to make sketching easier with a camera lucida.[2,3,4,5]

It was a letter in *Nicholson's Journal* comparing the camera lucida, disparagingly, with the camera obscura which brought forth the first really useful advice for the artist. T Sheldrake had bought a camera lucida after reading Wollaston's 'Description'; he wrote '...[I] made experiments to ascertain the extent of its merits compared with those of the Camera Obscura. I beg leave to send the result of these experiments... in hopes that they may induce the ingenious inventor of the Camera Lucida to bring it still nearer to perfection.'[6,7] (There is no record of Wollaston's reply!) Sheldrake wrote at length about how he found it impossible to observe the reflection of the object and

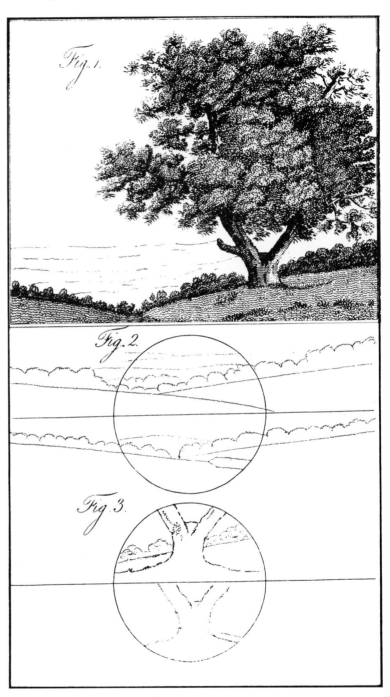

T Sheldrake's illustration and legend (opposite) for his letter on the inadequacy of the camera lucida. From *Nicholson's Journal* (1809).

References to the Drawing.

Fig. 1. Sketch from nature as it may be seen and drawn immediately in the camera obscura.

Fig. 2. Part of the same view as seen in the camera lucida; the upper half contains a portion of the horizontal lines in the view as reflected in the glass: the lower half shows the pencil imitating the same lines upon the paper, it is obvious that by looking diagonally into the glass the view may be extended so as to take in a portion of those lines which cannot be seen when looking directly into the glass.

Fig. 3. Part of the tree seen in the upper half reflected in the glass, the pencil copying the same parts upon the paper in the lower half. It is evident that no more of this object can be copied at one time than can be seen by looking directly into the glass, of course the whole tree cannot be seen at once, and cannot be copied without shifting the instrument several times, so as to take it by separate pieces, which cannot be *seen at one time*, consequently there is great danger of losing the truth of the whole, while one is employed on each part.

---

his pencil at the same time, and could not see the whole of his object without having to move the prism. He illustrated his letter with excellent drawings which showed exactly his error, of which he was unaware. It would appear that Sheldrake was experienced in the use of the camera obscura and it seems he was using the camera lucida in a somewhat similar manner. His eye was too far away from the prism so that he saw only a portion of his subject and could not maintain the precise position of the pupil looking in the prism and over the edge at the same time. The editor of the journal made a brief comment on Sheldrake's letter and referred to the importance of the eye position. However, R B Bate replied at length explaining the proper position of the eye, and the balance of illumination also giving instructions for dealing with tall objects.[8]

George Dollond's booklet on the camera lucida, mentioned on p. 22 included a long letter from Captain Basil Hall who had published a book of drawings made with the instrument.[9,10] The letter supplemented Dollond's technical description and gave sound advice to the draughtsman whilst pointing out '...that the Camera Lucida, though possessed of great powers, has no means of supplying taste, or industry to persons, who by nature are destitute of these gifts—neither will it enable people, who are totally ignorant of the use of the pencil, whatever be their talent, to make good drawings, without very considerable practice'. He pointed out that the instrument will assist in drawing 'Form, Proportion and Perspective' and '...will give as true representation of nature as any amateur, or perhaps, even any artist ought to aim at in a sketch.' Hall raised the point that some people think there is no

An illustration from Dollond's booklet, showing how to use a camera lucida with the table and stool which were also available. Wollaston's type of camera lucida with its two eyesight correcting lenses is shown in detail. The legends read 'Drawn by C Varley for G Dollond, with the Camera Lucida', and 'Engraved by J Gladwin, 8 Charles Street, Somers Town'. Varley's address was 1 Charles Street, Somers Town.

merit in a drawing made with a camera lucida, to which he said, 'But a little reflection will show, that the wish to gain credit for making sketches, is, or ought to be, altogether subordinate to the wish to represent natural objects correctly. And there is little fear that any amount of diligence or talent . . . will be able, even with the help of the Camera, to come up to nature—and so long as this point is not reached, no sketcher has any reason to complain that his task is so easy that it is unworthy of him.'

Cornelius Varley, in his *Treatise on Optical Drawing Instruments*, made similar remarks to those just quoted. However, he was mainly concerned with the application of his Graphic Telescope.[11] He said, 'When a back-ground is mountainous, sketching further off brings them up in a much grander proportion, and thus the telescope finds numerous views, that before were unnoticed . . . .' It is interesting to compare this statement with a footnote by Brewster in his book on the stereoscope, in which he writes

> Sir Francis Chantrey . . . shewed me . . . a Sketch-Book containing numerous drawings which he had made with a camera lucida . . . He pointed out to me the flatness or rather lowness, of the hills, which to his own eye appeared much higher, but which, not-withstanding, gave to him the idea of a greater elevation. In order to put this opinion to the test of experiment, I had drawings made by a skilful artist of the three Eldon hills . . . and was surprised to obtain, by comparing them with their true perspective outlines, a striking confirmation of the observation made by Sir Francis Chantrey.[12]

Brewster's experiment is, of course, a confirmation of the fact that the camera lucida, the Graphic Telescope and all optical drawing aids, including the photographic camera, always present a scene in true perspective; it may be very steep or very flat perspective but it is never distorted. As Varley wrote, 'This telescope will give all the views strictly correct, without any care or anxiety about perspective. . . .'

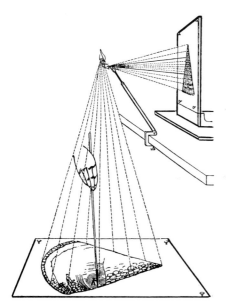

An illustration of the method for making an enlarged drawing with a Wollaston camera lucida. A convex lens would be placed in front of the prism in order to make the original appear as far from the eye as the pencil point. From Hogg, Jabez 1861 *The Elements of Experimental and Natural Philosophy*.

A drawing made with any camera lucida may be as large as desired, provided the distances of the object and the drawing paper are made compatible for the eye. We have referred to the ease with which the Graphic Telescope was adaptable for any distance of the drawing. In his *Treatise* Varley enlarged on this aspect by saying, 'The field of view of this instrument, when at eighteen inches below the eyepiece, is a circle of eighteen inches diameter, whether the power is much or little, but it may be as much larger as we choose to place the eyepiece above the paper or canvas. I have by this means had a six feet area, and marked out the sketch with charcoal at the end of a long reed stick, the paper and the telescope is therefore shifted for succeeding portions, and thereby we can make sketches several feet long.' A similar technique was described later in the century by the microscopist Dr J Anthony.[13]

The long correspondence, already mentioned, in the *Mechanics' Magazine* (1829–30) brought forth many comments on drawing and the utility of the camera lucida.[14] It was said of artists that it was 'used by most of them very privately'. However, the editor said that 'Captain Basil Hall has very honestly acknowledged the assistance he derived from this instrument... the number of acknowledgements would be greater, could every writer of travels afford as well as Captain H. to assume no more merit than really belongs to him.' It was suggested that the camera lucida would be of assistance to cabinet makers and artisans for '... to put even a chair into correct perspective, is no easy matter; but by means of the Camera Lucida, it may be done in less than five minutes'. The correct positioning of the head and eye was carefully explained. The following quotation is in respect of verifying a reproduced scale but the remarks apply equally to drawing. 'Observe, the eye should be placed as close to the glass prism as possible; and in looking at the ends of the scale, the head should not be turned, but a certain oblique ocular survey (commonly known by the name of *ogling*) should be made use of. And in order to prevent the slight motion of the head, which is apt to take place, the olfactory organ may be delicately placed in contact with the brass adjusting screw of the prism.' We think the 'delicacy' was more to prevent movement of the prism rather than possible damage to the 'olfactory organ'.

A fitting end for this chapter comes from Francis West's little book on the camera lucida.†[15]

> In short, if Dr. Wollaston, by his invention has not actually discovered a Royal road to drawing, he has at least succeeded in Macadamising the way already known.

References

1. Perspectograph (Messrs Rowney, artist's suppliers) *c.* 1980
2. *British Cyclopaedia* 1835 pp. 255–6
3. *Dictionary of the Arts, Sciences and Manufactures* 1842
4. *English Cyclopaedia* 1891 pp. 532–3
5. *Penny Cyclopaedia* 1836 p. 199
6. Sheldrake T 1809 On the camera lucida. letter *Nicholson's Journal (Journal of Natural Philosophy, Chemistry and the Arts)* **23** 372–7
7. Sheldrake T 1810 On the use of the camera lucida as a substitute for the camera lucida. letter *Journal of Natural Philosophy, Chemistry and the Arts* **25** 173–7
8. Bate R B 1809 On the camera lucida. letter *Journal of Natural Philosophy, Chemistry and the Arts* **24** 146–50
9. Dollond G *Description of the Camera Lucida, and Instruments for Drawing in True Perspective* nd. 1830?
10. Hall, Capt. Basil R N 1829 *Forty Etchings from Sketches made with the Camera Lucida in North America in 1827 and 1828*

†Taken from Captain Basil Hall's Memorandum in his book *Forty Etchings* etc (1829).

11. Varley, Cornelius 1845 *A Treatise on Optical Drawing Instruments*
12. Brewster D 1856 *The Stereoscope* p. 172
13. Anthony Dr J 1884 On drawing prisms *Journal of the Royal Microscopical Society* Ser. 2 **4** 697–703
14. *Mechanics' Magazine* 1829 **2** 381; 1830 **3** 354, 155, 345
15. West, Francis 1831 *Description of the Camera-Lucida*

Artists and the Camera Lucida

It may be argued that the camera lucida indirectly created one of the greatest impacts on the art world which, paradoxically, brought about the demise of the instrument. Through his impatience and inability to use a camera lucida W H Fox Talbot returned to the camera obscura, from which he subsequently developed the photographic camera.[1] About a hundred years later, when photography became extremely popular and a recognised art medium, the camera lucida no longer existed for the artist.

However, during the greater part of the hundred years prior to the 1930s the camera lucida flourished as a sketching aid for amateur and professional artists. No doubt it also played a part with the photographic camera in ousting the camera obscura for making drawings. Whatever the respective merits and rivalries of the three instruments may be, our purpose in this section is to mention some of the artists known to have used the camera lucida.

Captain Basil Hall RN (1788–1844) has already been referred to in connection with his letter of commendation published by the instrument makers Dollond and Francis West. During 1827 and 1828 the Captain made an extensive tour of North America, an account of which he published in 1829.[2] In the preface to his *Travels* he wrote 'During the journey, I had opportunities of making some sketches with the Camera Lucida, an instrument invented by the late Dr. Wollaston. But I have thought it best, instead of encumbering this

Griante
& the Chapel of S. Martino

A Sketch made by W H Fox Talbot whilst at Lake Como in 1833. It was dissatisfaction with the camera lucida that led Fox Talbot to attempt sketching with a camera obscura, and eventually to use that instrument for the photographic process he invented in 1839. From that time the photographic camera developed as a separate piece of apparatus from the camera obscura.

work with drawings of such slender pretensions, to publish, in a separate form, a selection of those which appeared most characteristic.' Thus we have his *Forty Etchings from Sketches made with the Camera Lucida in North America in 1827 and 1828* which is, in effect, an illustrated supplement to his three-volume work.[3] Whilst we may accept Hall's modest appraisal of his drawings, for they do present a certain naivety, there is no question of their veracity as records of people and

90

places. We may regret, as did the Editor of the *Mechanics' Magazine*, that more travellers did not have their camera lucida sketches printed as drawn, rather than hand them to an engraver who worked the sketch up into a conventional pictorial composition. We suspect this was the case with Smyth and Lowe when making their South American tour.[4] The situation is different and more acceptable for the professional artist who makes engravings or lithographs from his own sketches.

The sailing ship *Royal George* was launched in 1756 and it sank in Portsmouth Harbour in 1782; a capstan was recovered from the wreck in 1839. Mr Augustin Creuze, of Her Majesty's Dockyard, Portsmouth, wrote a technical note on the capstan and its condition, with an illustration by Captain Hall.[5] The note was published in the *United Service Journal* for November 1839. The Captain's letter accompanying the sketch was in much the same vein as the advertisement for Dollond and West. However, his final sentence is not without interest, 'The drawing of the Royal George's capstan . . . occupied me not quite three-quarters of an hour, yet, I will undertake to say it is as correct in all essential particulars as if it had been drawn by a professed artist.'

George Cumberland Jnr went to Spain and Portugal during the Peninsular War, and whilst in Portugal received a letter from his antiquarian friend C A Stothard.[6] The letter, dated London 1810, contained a request, 'There are several things I wish to hear about in your next; I should like to know how you succeed with the Camera, whether you find it of great use, what objects you have chosen for the pencil, what antiquities you have found in the churches, whether you have seen any monuments relating to dresses and armour.' The British Library has a slim sketch book titled *Views in Spain and Portugal taken during the campaigns of His Grace the Duke of Wellington by George Cumberland, Jr., only 30 copies printed.*[7] The style of the drawings is

A drawing by Captain Basil Hall of a capstan retrieved in 1839 from the sailing ship *Royal George* which sank in Portsmouth Harbour in 1782.

91

Venus fishing. An illustration from Sir William Gell's book on the ruins and ornaments of Pompeii, published in 1832.

very similar to those of Captain Hall though there is no written evidence of the use of a camera lucida; they are mostly signed, 'Drawn and etched by G. Cumberland, Jr'.

Sir William Gell (1777–1836) was a much more accomplished artist than Captain Hall but he too was concerned with the making of exact records. In the preface to his book on the antiquities of Pompeii, Gell stated, 'The views and pictures have been uniformly made by the Author, as before, with the prism of Dr. Wollaston, and the drawings have been compared with such copies of the originals as have been published in the Museo Borbonico at Naples.'[8] Furthermore all the illustrations are duplicated as etchings and engravings! The picture of the Tepidarium was acknowledged to another artist, 'In the view, Plate XXIX which is copied, by permission from a large drawing made with the camera lucida by my friend M. Zahn, architectural painter to the Elector of Hess Cassel. . . .'

Egypt in the early part of the last century was a great tourist attraction. The visitors then were not mere sightseers but mostly young men, artists and architects, eager to record and learn from the monuments and structures of the ancients. John Romer described these explorers in his book *Valley of the Kings* (1981), saying that many were skilled draughtsmen who frequently used a camera lucida.[9] Among the names Romer mentions are Hoskins and Catherwood.

G A Hoskins in company with Robert Hay and Frederick Catherwood made an expedition to Oasis Magna in the Libyan desert in 1832 and later he published an account of the journey.[10] In the Preface, Hoskins wrote, 'The plates are selected from a large portfolio of drawings, made by the Author with the Camera Lucida, and finished on the spot.' The plates are lithographs usually signed by a firm of lithographers, though occasionally the individual artist–lithographer is mentioned.

Frederick Catherwood (1799–1854) was an architect

of extraordinary resources yet, sadly, a man of great misfortune.[11] He had a considerable scholarship and love for the ancient monuments of Egypt and South America, and used a camera lucida when making precise and detailed records; his choice of viewpoint and composition are worthy of a professional artist. Through his misfortunes very little is known of Catherwood, and much of his work was destroyed in a fire, but we have an interesting anecdote from one of his letters concerning the Mosque of Omar, 'I had long adopted the usual dress of an Egyptian officer . . . I determined to take in [to the Mosque] my camera lucida, and sit down and make a drawing. . . We entered and arranging the camera, I quickly sat down to my work, not without some nervousness, as I perceived the Musselmen, from time to time, mark me with doubtful looks . . . .'[12] The situation became quite nasty with a crowd angry at the trespass of an infidel. However, Catherwood and his servant were saved by the timely arrival of the Governor, with whom he had 'smoked and become intimate'.

Sir John Herschel, a friend of Fox Talbot and fellow member of the Lunar Society, made a number of sketches and drawings whilst in South Africa during the years 1834 to 1838.[13] Many of the sketches are signed and noted 'del. Cam. Luc.' (delineated by camera lucida) and Herschel's diary (1 February 1834) refers to the instrument, 'Then Took a camera sketch of the superb Mountains in front of our house. . .'. Again for the entry on 18 May 1837, 'Planned & put in hand with the Carpenter a Panorama Drawing board (a pair) to hold many papers ready for Camera work.' Although Sir John is known for his scientific work, especially in astronomy, he had considerable artistic ability. Many of the drawings made with the aid of his Wollaston-type camera lucida show free-hand pencil work by the inclusion of figures and animals, even a prancing pony. Lady Herschel also sketched, and she coloured some of her husband's flower drawings, which

The Temple of Juno at Girgenti, Sicily. A drawing by Sir John Herschel with the aid of a Wollaston camera lucida, 1824.

although made as botanical records nevertheless have a delicate and sensitive arrangement.

We have already mentioned Cornelius Varley as one who was almost equally a scientist and artist. He exhibited at the Royal Academy on occasions from 1803 until 1859 when he was about 78 years of age. The British Museum Print Room has a number of Varley's portrait and landscape drawings; many are large, about 600 × 400 mm. Frequently they are signed 'Drawn by Cornelius Varley with Graphic Telescope' or similar wording.

S D Kitson, in his paper on Dawson Turner's collection of portrait drawings, referred to the Graphic Telescope and made the extraordinary statement, 'A modification of Varley's telescope called the 'camera

94

Mrs Cornelius Varley. 'Drawn by C Varley with his Patent Graphic Telescope'. Unfortunately this study of the artist's wife is not dated.

lucida', is still sold by artists' colourmen.'[14] The latter part we do believe, but it was only for a few more years that the camera lucida of the prism type remained in the shops. Several portrait drawings are reproduced with Kitson's notes. Among them are two by John

Cornelius Varley wrote on this portrait, 'Dr Spurzheim the introducer of Phrenology into England, traced from life with Graphic Telescope by Cornelius Varley 1815'.

Varley, of John Bannister (1760–1836) and of Dr Thomas Monro (1759–1833); both have a 'Graphic Telescope' inscription.

A portrait of the Bristol-born artist James Baker Pyne (1800–70) is signed 'From a drawing finished by James Ward, R.A. (1769–1859) after a sketch taken by Varley's Cam. Lucida.' This portrait is at the County Central Library, Bristol.

96

John Sell Cotman (1782–1842) is, perhaps, the most famous artist known to have used a camera lucida. He was one of the group of young men who gathered at Dr Monro's house in London, where he became acquainted with John and Cornelius Varley. Dawson Turner, a banker at Great Yarmouth, employed Cotman as a drawing master for his wife and two daughters; he was also the artist's patron and together they published sketches of the churches and antiquities of Normandy. Mrs Turner and her four daughters accompanied Cotman on his second Normandy tour in 1818.[15]

Before setting out alone on his first trip to Normandy in 1817 Cotman was presented with a camera lucida by Sir Henry Englefield and he took it with him.[16] H Isherwood Kay wrote in the Walpole Society Papers 'As Cotman was starting [for Normandy], his old friend Sir Henry Englefield gave him a Camera Lucida, the newest aid to drawing in perspective. Finally perfected by Dr. Wollaston in 1812 [*sic*] for the use of topographical draughtsmen, its adoption by 'all ye artists' in London, especially by the sculptor Chantrey, was a surprise to Cotman, and even now is not generally known.' This may be the source for Kitson's 'modification' statement quoted above in the paragraph on Cornelius Varley. Kay was referring to Cotman's letter to Dawson Turner in which he says of Sir Henry's gift '... also a Camera Lucida like yours ...'.

In a letter to Dawson Turner, Cotman wrote, 'I did not finish the Cathedral till Wednesday, and now it is all to redraw for it is all on separate pieces of paper, and nearly all of it done with the camera lucida which I did not know how to manage.'[15] At Rouen, Cotman met the young architect Charles Barry (1795–1860) who returned with him to his hotel. Barry wrote in his diary, '... where he showed me a very large and new-invented Camera Lucida by Varley'.[17] From this diary entry it has been supposed that Cotman used Varley's Graphic Telescope. This is not unreasonable

in view of Cotman's letter to Dawson Turner in which
he says the drawing of the Cathedral '... is all on
separate pieces of paper'. We can well imagine how
tiresome it must have been adjusting the Graphic
Telescope so many times because it could not possibly
take in the whole cathedral in one view. Even at the
lowest power of the telescope (4) it would cover only
one sixteenth of the area visible to the eye, and one
should really think in terms of a single eye view. Many
authorities have assumed, and we too are inclined to
believe, that Barry's description refers to the Graphic
Telescope. Nevertheless it does seem odd that neither
Barry nor Cotman refer to it by that name, and in
Cotman's case it is especially surprising since he knew
Cornelius Varley.

On the second Normandy tour, when Cotman was
joined by Mrs Turner and her daughters, he again had
a camera lucida. One of the girls, Elizabeth, also had a
camera lucida which Mrs Turner used on occasion. We
may wonder whether this was her father's instrument
(which was like Cotman's) or whether it was her own
(perhaps a prism camera lucida)? In the letters sent to
Dawson Turner by his wife, Elizabeth, Mary Anne
(another daughter) and Cotman the 'camera lucida' is
mentioned eight (possibly more) times—not once the
'Graphic Telescope'. Mary Anne's letter to her father
makes it quite clear that the party had two instruments,
'Mr. Cotman and Elizabeth had hardly begun their
drawings with their camera lucidas when it began to
rain violently and entirely put a stop to their proceedings.' Mrs Turner wrote, '... there is no drawing with
the Camera Lucida with a bonnet on, and even when
that is removed it is needful to hold up the hair away
from the forehead...'. It is possible that a bonnet
large enough to ward off the sun's heat would cast a
shadow over the drawing paper and so upset the
balance of illumination. However, it is more likely that
the real nuisance of a bonnet with either a Graphic
Telescope or a Wollaston camera lucida was the brim.

It would hit the telescope tube and prevent the eye approaching the eyepiece mirror, and it would cover the prism of the latter instrument. The instrument maker R B Bate made a point of this in his 1809 letter, 'Though hitherto omitted, it is proper to notice the frequent impediments to an extent of view, arising from the obstruction of near objects, parts of the head-dress in particular are sometimes unsuspected obstructions and the brim of the hat the most formidable of all.'†[18]

Mrs Turner's hair would have been no bother with a Graphic Telescope, it would merely fall about the tube. A prism camera lucida would be useless, as she says, because her hair would fall in front of the prism and obstruct the view. Mrs Turner also referred to the camera lucida as 'a perverse little instrument' and that Mary Anne had to serve as a screen against a window, '... for Elizabeth to see the staircase...'.[19] Both comments are appropriate to the use of a prism rather than the Graphic Telescope.

Elizabeth wrote, 'We were up at half past five this morning, and went to St. Ouen, where we were admitted into the gardens... I made a tolerably accurate outline with the camera lucida of the east end, which I hope to finish on the spot, for that is the only way to do it the little justice I can.'[15] We do not know how big a building St Ouen was (or is), but it is difficult to imagine that a Graphic Telescope would have encompassed the east end from within the gardens for Elizabeth to make an outline and to finish on the spot. Furthermore it seems obvious she was dealing with only one piece of paper.

In view of Mrs Turner's struggles with bonnet, hair and camera lucida it is interesting to read part of a

---

†We are reminded of John Cuff who gave similar advice in respect of the microscope, 'But whatever light you use, be very careful not to shade the Object with your hat or periwig.' *Description of a Pocket Microscope* 1743.

letter from the artist T Phillips to her husband written about two years earlier. 'Geo. Str. Aug. 4 1815. My Dear Sr . . . I amused myself in the garden with the Camera Lucida which though I had seen it I had not used before . . . Mr. Cotman I think took one down with him. Does Mrs. Turner or Elizabeth ever use it, or do they disdain such mechanical . . .'.[20]

For our present purpose we are interested only in Cotman's use of a camera lucida, whether it was Varley's Graphic Telescope or a prism will probably never be resolved with certainty.

The Normandy tour was not the only occasion Cotman used the instrument. The Phillips letter was written in 1815, and Charles J Palmer, FSA, a solicitor at Great Yarmouth, and an acquaintance of Dawson Turner, recorded in his diary/journal (1825), 'April 28 – Mr. Cotman, the artist, has done me the favour to take my likeness in pencil with a camera lucida.'[21] When he was about eight or nine years old Palmer received drawing lessons from 'Mr. John Sell Cotman, an artist who has subsequently distinguished himself by his architectural publications.'

Sir Francis Chantrey (1781–1841), a sculptor who amassed a considerable fortune which he bequeathed to the Royal Academy, made some of his preliminary drawings for portrait busts with the aid of a camera lucida. As in the case of Cotman, some doubt exists as to the type of camera lucida he used (in fact more than that, the alternative instrument may not have been a camera lucida at all!).

Chantrey's comment to Dr Brewster on the difference of perspective in a camera lucida drawing and a drawing by eye has already been mentioned in the chapter on drawing with a camera lucida (p. 85). An artist when sketching, and the layman when looking at the countryside, will always *see* mountains higher than they really are by true perspective, as in a photograph or when drawn with a camera lucida.

Charles Robert Leslie, RA (1794–1859) wrote in his

Reproduced from a lithograph titled 'WOLLASTON. From a sketch (made with the camera lucida) by Chantrey. Drawn on Stone by R J Lane.' It is signed 'To Edward Codrington with Frs. Chantrey's respects'. Reproduced by permission of the Royal College of Physicians. The 'stone' is at the Science Museum, South Kensington.

---

journal (*c.* 1836), 'July 31st In the evening I went to Mr. Dunlop's. Mr. Dunlop had been sitting to Chantrey, who fixed the back of his head in a wooden machine to keep him perfectly still, and then drew with a Camera Lucida the profile and front face of the size of life.'[22] There is also the reference to a camera lucida in the letter from T Phillips to Dawson Turner already mentioned in respect of Cotman. The previous sentence reads, 'I dined with Sr. Jos. Banby on Sunday last & went to Spring Grove with Chantrey the sculptor who is modelling a bust of him & has made it very like & a very good head too. I amused myself in the garden with the Camera Lucida . . . .' We presume it to have been Chantrey's instrument.

In 1849 George Jones, RA, published his book 'Sir Francis Chantrey, R.A. Recollections of his Life, Practice and Opinions'.[23] In the Appendix Jones quotes an account given him by Sir Henry Russell (1783–1852), son of the famous Indian judge (also Sir Henry Russell), 'My first intercourse with Sir Francis, then Mr. Chantrey . . . began by my sitting to him in 1822, for a bust. . . He had already given up executing busts on private orders; but he was still willing to undertake such as were required for public purposes.' Obviously Chantrey was quite well off by this time. The account continued, 'The first day, he only made a rough sketch of the face, using for the purpose an instrument with a tube, through which he looked, while, with a pencil fixed in one arm of it, he traced an outline of the full size on paper.' Russell does not use the term 'camera lucida', he said it was an 'instrument with a tube'. This could refer to Varley's Graphic Telescope, but 'with a pencil fixed in one arm of it' does not apply to any form of camera lucida yet discovered in our researches.

The passage, although brief, exactly describes the 'Optigraph', an instrument we prefer to associate with perspective delineators. A delineator works on the principle that whilst the eye views a scene from a fixed position a pointer is moved around the outline of objects in the scene. The other end of the pointer carries a pencil in contact with a sheet of paper. As the pointer moves so the pencil makes a corresponding mark on the paper.

The 'Optigraph' was first designed by Jesse Ramsden. On Ramsden's death Thomas Jones took up the instrument and improved it so that large or small drawings could be made of an object at a given distance. Jones, an instrument maker in Mount Street,

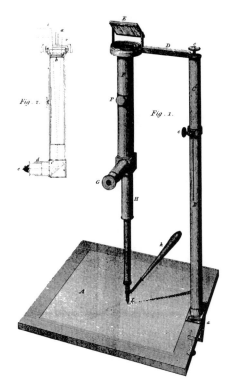

The Optigraph, a perspective delineator made by Thomas Jones and described by him in 1807. The original simple instrument was designed by Jesse Ramsden, the eighteenth-century astronomical instrument maker.

Berkley Square, described the improved Optigraph in 1807.[24] It consisted of a vertical tube suspended by a universal joint from a fixed mirror at 45°. A small dot on a clear glass part way along the tube was observed by an eyepiece. By moving the tube about the universal joint the dot could be moved around the outline of the scene reflected in the stationary mirror. The end of the tube carried a pencil which was always in contact with a sheet of paper. The 'arm' was, in fact, a sort of handle at the pencil end of the tube by which it was moved. The Optigraph does not allow the user to see the point of his or her pencil moving over the area of the landscape or object.

We have described this instrument at some length in order to explain that whilst it is perfectly correct to call Varley's Graphic Telescope a camera lucida it is not so with the Optigraph. However, it must be emphasised that only Russell's description fits that instrument, and he was recalling from 25 years previously.

H Isherwood Kay's paper (1925–6) mentioned above in respect of Cotman also referred to Chantrey.[16] It said that the camera lucida, 'Finally perfected by Dr. Hyde Wollaston in 1812...' was adopted by artists '...especially by the sculptor Chantrey...'. A footnote on the same page said, 'Chantrey came to depend greatly upon the instrument for preparatory studies.' It appears that Kay thought Chantrey used Wollaston's 'perfected' camera lucida. However, speculation is pointless because he gave no reference to support his statement of Chantrey's dependance upon the instrument, a statement made nearly a hundred years after Chantrey died.

James Pattison Cockburn (1779?–1847), a military man and talented water-colourist, is said to have used a

103

camera lucida. The only real evidence we have is of him using some form of drawing aid. Louis Spohr, the composer, wrote in his *Autobiography* that whilst travelling in Italy in 1817 there was in the coach an Englishman '... possessed of an extraordinary skill in taking the fine views in a few minutes. For this purpose he made use of a machine which transmitted the landscape on a reduced scale to the paper ... we saw the whole method of his proceeding, which afforded infinite pleasure to the children... He gave me his address: Major Cockburn, Woolwich, nine miles from London.'[25] Because Spohr and his children saw the method and it gave them pleasure it has recently been suggested that the 'machine' may have been a camera obscura.[26]

Juxta Turrim writing in 1865 in *Notes and Queries* said that in Cockburn's published volumes of scenery '... there is no mention of any remarkable method of transferring scenery to paper'. We confirm this statement, however, in the same year J.E.T. wrote 'The process by which this gentleman [Cockburn] made his drawings, as described in Spohr's Autobiography, was no doubt by the use of the *camera lucida* ....'[27]

This was interpreted by the *Dictionary of National Biography* (1908) as, '... that Cockburn was in the habit of using the camera lucida to ensure exactness of landscape detail.'[28]

Spendlove (1954) wrote '... Cockburn used a camera lucida. This ingenious instrument was used in a primitive form as early as the *Sixteenth Century*, but was re-discovered and improved by Dr. W. H. Wollaston in the early Nineteenth Century. In its improved form it consisted of an arrangement of mirrors or a prism of unusual shape... The right and left sides of the image would be transposed when seen in the camera lucida.'[29] Spendlove continued, '[the artist] ... would make a tracing in the instrument and then make a free-hand sketch from the tracing, reversing the right and left sides of the picture. Only a talented and capable artist

104

could do good work with this instrument . . .' and so on. He then quoted from Captain Basil Hall's book; it will be remembered that the Captain used a Wollaston-type camera lucida.

In 1976 Schoenherr wrote, 'Cockburn's prolific output may be the result of his use of some optical aid such as the camera lucida. . .'.[30] Our final quotation is from Bell and Cooke (1978) who thought Cockburn used an optical aid '. . . (possibly a *camera lucida*) . . . Through a combination of prism and lenses, a *camera lucida* enables an artist to trace the view . . . by projecting an image . . . .'[31]

It is fairly obvious that these writers knew of the camera lucida by name only.

It has recently been discovered that the 'reversed' drawings mentioned by Spendlove are accidental off-sets resulting from the type of ink used by Cockburn and long contact of a sheet of paper on his drawing. For this information we are indebted to Mr Didier Prioul of Quebec who is researching Cockburn's work for a doctoral thesis.

In conclusion we submit that Spohr's description, the only direct evidence, may be applied equally to a camera obscura or a camera lucida.

Samuel Butler (1835–1902) was the grandson and biographer of Samuel Butler the Bishop of Lichfield and Coventry, an important divine of the eighteenth century. A one-time New Zealand sheep farmer, Butler wrote satirical novels, attacked Darwinism, was a painter of note, a musician and composer.[32] In 1882 he wrote to his admirer and friend Miss Savage, '. . . I have got a painting fit on. I have got a new toy called a camera lucida which does all the drawing for me, and am so pleased with it that I am wanting to use it continually.'[33] She replied in a style and humour which is typical of her letters. 'Has a camera lucida anything to do with lucidity?

> Lucidity, lucidity,
> We seek it with avidity.

If it has you need not mention it to me again.' When Miss Savage died in 1885 his letters to her were returned to him; on the one quoted above he made a note, 'What a lot of time I wasted over that camera lucida to be sure! . . . -S.B. Dec. 14th 1901.' In his notebooks Butler made a brief reference to the camera lucida in connection with a visit to a London ale house, 'I went into Fleet Street one Sunday morning with my camera lucida to see whether I should like to make a sketch of the gap made by the demolition of the Cock Tavern.'[34]

H Festing Jones has written extensively about his friend Samuel Butler. He said of a short trip abroad in 1883, 'He brought back many more sketches than usual because he drew with a camera lucida, but it distorted the perspective and had to be given up.' Jones used the camera lucida to make a sketch from a window in Butler's rooms in London, it is reproduced in his *Memoir*. Butler bought the camera lucida in Paris on his way home from Verona in 1882. The instrument is signed 'Secretan', and is now in the Samuel Butler Collection, St John's College, Cambridge.[35]

John Ruskin made two comments on the camera lucida, they are both isolated statements and the first is curious, 'Chamouni, day 13th, Monday, June 25th [1849]—Up rather late this morning, and lost time before breakfast over camera-lucida; drove to Argen-tiere with my mother . . .'. The second reference tells us about Ruskin as a member of society, 'In blaming myself . . . for want of affection to other people, I must also express continually . . . more and more wonder that ever anybody had any affection for *me*. I thought they might as well have got fond of a camera-lucida, or an ivory foot-rule.'[36]

It is inevitable that the biographer of an artist should note and discuss any change of style or technique the artist may have had. James Roundell in his book on the water-colourist Thomas Shotter Boys (1803–74) dis-cusses two pencil drawings of the Pont Royal, one from the Institute the other including the Quai d'Orsay.[37] The former he says is a free-hand drawing and the latter has '... the absolute precision [which] makes it completely different and almost inartistic'. Roundell suggests this '... could be explained by the use of the Graphic Telescope...'. He goes on to say that the Graphic Telescope was used by E W Cooke, of whom Boys was a close friend, and, 'It is reasonable to *assume* [our italics] that Boys knew of its existence if he had not actually used it. The Telescope had a wide-angle lens and gave just the sort of viewpoint obtained by Boys in this drawing [*Pont Royal and the Quai d'Orsay*]. The wide expanse of foreground, though curiously attractive is inartistic and the whole appearance of the drawing is mechanical. It is *possible* [our italics] that Boys also used the Telescope for his engravings.'

The only reference Roundell gives for these comments is for the Graphic Telescope; it is a secondary reference and does not explain how the instrument works.[38] We may quibble over his use of the word 'viewpoint' which means the point or position of viewing not the view itself. However, much more important is the statement, 'The Telescope had a wide-angle lens...' which is a contradiction. The concepts of a telescopic view and a wide-angle view are incompatible. Roundell's reference makes no mention of a wide-angle lens and it does not appear in Varley's patent specification or in his description of the Graphic Telescope.[39,40]

It may well be that the drawing was made with a camera lucida of the prism type for which Wollaston claimed a view angle of about 70°.[41] We estimate the angle of view of the drawing, as reproduced, to be 70° to 80°, and there appears to be a slight distortion at the extremities of the drawing. However, the subject and the lines of the drawing are so simple that it could have been constructed by an artist versed in the rules of perspective.

We can conclude our discussion of artists and the

camera lucida as follows.

During the eighteenth century the most popular drawing aid was the camera obscura, almost every instrument maker in London showed it on his trade card. The camera lucida appeared in 1807 and not only supplanted the camera obscura but, we are quite certain, was in even greater demand.

The advent of photography in 1839 did little to curb the enthusiasm for the camera lucida until the 1920s and 1930s when the facility of the photographic camera caused a general decline in drawing and sketching as a hobby.

The comparatively large number of camera lucidas in museums and at the sale rooms indicates that during its heyday it was almost as popular, and perhaps as frequently used, as the photographic camera of today.

References

1. Talbot W H Fox 1844 *Pencil of Nature* (Da Capo, NY, Facsimile edn, 1969)
2. Hall, Capt. Basil, RN 1829 *Travels in North America* 3 vols
3. Hall, Capt. Basil, RN 1829 *Forty Etchings from Sketches Made with the Camera Lucida in North America in 1827 and 1828*
4. Smyth, Lt., RN and Lowe, Frederick 1836 *Narrative of a Journey from Lima to Para, Across the Andes and Down the Amazon, etc*
5. Hall, Capt. Basil, RN 1839 *Drawing and Description of the Capstan Lately Recovered from the Royal George* British Library shelf mark 8807bb41(3)
6. Stothard Mrs C A 1823 *Memoir ... of C. A. Stothard, F.S.A.*
7. Cumberland, George Jnr nd. ?1815 *Views in Spain and Portugal Taken During the Campaigns of His Grace the Duke of Wellington, By George Cumberland, Jr., Only 30 Copies Printed*
8. Gell Sir Wm 1832 *Pompeiana* pp. 23, 109
9. Romer, John 1981 *Valley of the Kings* (London: Michael Joseph/Rainbird) pp. 107–14
10. Hoskins G A 1837 *Visit to the Great Oasis of the Libyan Desert* pp. 8, 35

11. Hagen, Victor Wolfgang von 1950 *F. Catherwood* (Barre, MA: Barre) pp. 9–12

12. Bartlett W H 1844 *Walks about the City and Environs of Jerusalem* pp. 148, 162

13. Evans D S *et al* (eds) 1969 *Herschel at the Cape* (Texas) pp. 42–3, 305 Pls. 7–20

14. Kitson S D 1932–3 *Notes on a Collection of Portrait Drawings formed by Dawson Turner* (Oxford: Walpole Society/Oxford University Press) p. 102

15. Kitson S D 1937 *John Sell Cotman* (London: Faber) pp. 120–251

16. Kay H Isherwood 1925–6 *John Sell Cotman's letters from Normandy* (Walpole Society/Oxford University Press) pp. 93–4

17. Bolton A T 1939 letter, Cotman and Charles Barry in Rouen *Journal of the Royal Institute of British Architects* 795

18. Bate R B 1809 On the camera lucida. letter *Journal of Natural Philosophy, Chemistry and the Arts* **24** 146–50

19. Rajnai, Miklos and Allthorpe-Guyton, Marjorie 1975 Drawings of Normandy in Norwich Castle Museum, Norwich (5)

20. Letter, T Phillips to Dawson Turner 1815 (Trinity College Library, Cambridge)

21. Palmer F D 1892 *Leaves from the Diary and Journal of the Late Charles J. Palmer, F.S.A.* pp. 12, 37

22. Taylor T (ed) 1860 *Autobiographical Recollections by the late Charles Robert Leslie, R.A.* p. 152

23. Jones, George 1849 *Sir Francis Chantrey, R.A. Recollections of his Life, Practice and Opinions* p. 275–7

24. Jones, Thomas 1807 Description of the optigraph *Philosophical Magazine* **27** 66–9 Pl. 28

25. Spohr L 1865 *Autobiography* (translated from the German) reprint 1969 (New York: Da Capo) p. 33

26. Hammond J H 1981 *Camera Obscura* (Bristol: Adam Hilger) p. 130 (Spohr's dates are in error)

27. *Notes and Queries* 1865 letter pp. 6, 309, 406

28. *Dictionary of National Biography* 1908

29. Spendlove F St George 1954 The Canadian watercolours of James Pattison Cockburn *The Connoisseur* (April) 203–7

30. Schoenherr D E 1976 *Picturesque Quebec 1826–1832. Views by James Pattison Cockburn* Public Archives of Canada

31. Bell, Michael and Cooke, W Martha 1978 *The Last 'Lion' —Rambles in Quebec with James Pattison Cockburn* exhibition catalogue, Agnes Etherington Art Centre, Ontario

32. *Dictionary of National Biography* 2nd Supplement 1912 (reprinted 1920) (Oxford: Oxford University Press)

33. Jones H Festing 1919 *Samuel Butler, Author of Erewhon (1803–1902) a Memoir* vol. 1 pp. 376–9
34. Jones H Festing (ed) 1912 *Notebooks of Samuel Butler* p. 122
35. Letter from the Librarian, St John's College, Cambridge
36. Ruskin, John *Works* (library edn) vol. 35 pp. 455, 457
37. Roundell, James 1974 *Thomas Shotter Boys* (London: Octopus) pp. 35, 90
38. Pidgley, Michael 1972 Cornelius Varley, Cotman and the graphic telescope *Burlington Magazine* (November) 781–6
39. Varley, Cornelius 1811 *British Patent* No 3430
40. Varley, Cornelius 1845 *A Treatise on Optical Drawing Instruments*
41. Wollaston W H 1807 Description of the camera lucida *Journal of Natural Philosophy, Chemistry and the Arts* **17** 1–5 Pl. 1; also *Philosophical Magazine* **27** 343–7 Pl. 8.

Part Two

The Camera Lucida and the Microscope

Illustration overleaf from a Lechertier Barbe leaflet.

Instrumentation

Introduction

Modern accounts of microscopical research are usually illustrated with photographs or electron micrographs; some scientists, however, prefer to make drawings of their material. Drawings are specific, they clarify the intention of the text and are not cluttered with inessential details as are photographs. On occasion both a photograph and a drawing will be used, this is perhaps the ideal situation where the photograph shows what may be seen in the microscope and the drawing aids the textual explanation. Microscopists have always had the problem of communicating their observations and conclusions visually. Almost from the beginning of microscopy in the seventeenth century, drawings were made in order to supplement a written description. Some of the drawings may appear crude and naive but there is little doubt that for the readers at the time they added further information.

In a review of microscopical communication G L'E Turner referred to and quoted Robert Hooke and Anton van Leeuwenhoek, two seventeenth-century scientists of whom we know a great deal.[1] As draughtsmen or artists they probably represent the extremes of ability. Hooke was a very fine draughtsman, the plates in his book will always be regarded as superb illustrations. Leeuwenhoek, on the other hand, was quite hopeless. Fortunately he was aware of his inadequacy and employed an artist to make drawings for his publications. This was not an uncommon practice, though, of course, there were many problems involved, not the least being the artist's skill at using a microscope and

■ 1718. *Animal.* JOBLOT, Descr .... Microscopes ....
Avec.... obs. .... d'Insectes. &c.; Paris. — v. 2. c. 28. p. 57.
„D'une infusion d'anémone .... préparée .... avec de l'eau
commune" (d. w. z. slootwater!) ....
dans une goutte .... un animal
nouveau .... Planche 6, marqué 12. —
Tout le dessus de son corps est couvert
d'un beau masque bien formé, de
figure humaine, parfaitement bien
fait; .... six pattes et une queuë,
sortant de dessous de ce masque,
qui est couronné d'une coëffure sin-
gulière."

The first drawing of a hydrachnid larva. This drawing was made
by Louis Joblot (1645–1723), Professor of Mathematics at the
French Royal Academy of Painting and Sculpture. Joblot is said
to be the first French microscopist. From Oudemans A C 1926
Kritische Historische Overzicht der Acarologie (Leiden).

interpreting the image in the same manner as the
scientist. The progress of the drawing required constant supervision, and there was yet another stage
before the final reproduction. In order to make a print
the drawing had to be transferred to a wood block or
metal plate or, in the last century, to a stone for
lithography. In all three processes the drawing had to
be reversed. Thus there are microscopical illustrations,
made in the eighteenth and nineteenth centuries, which
may be third-hand interpretations of the original
material. Almost certainly most of the illustrations will
be at second hand for there were very few, if any,
microscopists who were equally artists and engravers.
Engravings and lithographs were usually signed by the
artist or delineator (del.) and the engraver (eng.) or
lithographer (lith.), occasionally 'stone' was used in
place of lithography.

Robert Hooke described his method of working
when drawing; first he studied the appearance of a
subject from many angles, then, having chosen a view,
he looked at it many times in order to memorise the

A silverfish, *Lepisma saccharina*, one of the most primitive of insects. The engraving is reproduced from the *Micrographia* of Robert Hooke (1667), who wrote, 'It is a small white Silver-shining Worm or Moth, which I found conversant among Books and Papers...'.

appearance and form. He would then make a drawing, compare it with the microscope image, and redraw or add amendments. No doubt this technique was followed by many of Hooke's contemporaries; and, we will discover, was recommended in the last century. It is possible to observe the microscope image with one eye and the pencil and paper with the other, but it is very tiring. This is particularly so when the microscope illumination is by candle or oil lamp, as it generally was during dull winter days and at night in the seventeenth and eighteenth centuries.

Sunlight as an aid to drawing became available to the microscopist with the advent of the solar microscope in the 1730s. Initially the instrument was used for projecting microscopic images in a darkened room but it was soon realised that the image could be projected onto a screen as in a camera obscura. To trace the image thus formed entailed very little skill, and scientists had direct control of whatever they wished to show in their drawings. Although the drawing had to be submitted to an engraver or lithographer one stage of interpretation was eliminated, so microscopists had closer control over the final result. Unfortunately solar microscopes were expensive. Ideally a clockwork mechanism was required to adjust the angle of a mirror reflecting the ever-changing position of the sun. Paradoxically the greatest disadvantage was the sun itself, which could not be relied upon to shine when required.

In 1771 the instrument maker Benjamin Martin made and sold a simple telescope and microscope which had a glass disc ruled in squares, mounted in the focus of the eyepiece.[2] The shapes seen in a particular square were drawn in the corresponding square of a lightly ruled sheet of paper. Martin's pamphlet des-

115

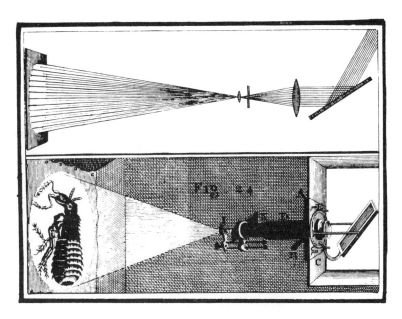

A hand-operated solar microscope. The flea was a common subject for microscope viewing and projection in the eighteenth century. From l'Abbe Nollet 1756 *Leçons de Physique Experimentale*.

---

cribing the 'Graphical Perspective and Microscope' referred to artists drawing insects for his periodical the *General Magazine of Arts and Sciences* and that he '. . . was amazed to find the difficulty and trouble which such an unusual undertaking gave them. I could never have thought that a late celebrated designer and engraver would have found it necessary to make 3 or 4 drawings of a Bug only, before he could produce one wherein the keeping, or symmetry and proportion of the parts was tolerably well observed, and that in not less than 10 or 12 days time.' With the Graphical Microscope, Martin wrote, the same insect '. . . might have been drawn and finished in less than so many hours . . .'.

It is interesting to note that neither Wollaston (1806) nor Amici (1819) referred to the design of a camera lucida specifically for use with the microscope in their original papers. This is surprising since they were both interested in the microscope; Wollaston only in respect

Wollaston's camera lucida in use. This illustration was taken from the 1857 catalogue of Messrs Ross (the microscope is of the old 250 mm tube length).

of his 'periscopic'[†] lens but Amici was involved in the design and manufacture of microscopes. The latter's paper 'Le Camere Lucide' (1819) commented upon 'ordinary' camera lucidas adapted to the microscope and telescope, and he said 'Which I propose to look into on another occasion.'[3] A camera lucida adaption is mentioned in Amici's paper on a reflecting microscope (1820). The first reference to the use of a camera lucida with a microscope was made in 1809 in the letter by the instrument maker R B Bate which was mentioned earlier (see p. 99).[4] Bate concluded his letter by saying that the camera lucida may be used with a microscope in the horizontal position and with a telescope. This was less than three years after Wollaston's patent, and as no other type of camera lucida has been discovered from that time we must assume that Bate was referring to Wollaston's camera lucida. Although he says 'may be used' there is little doubt that he, as an instrument maker, had experimented with Wollaston's prism attached to a microscope.

[†]Wollaston W H 1812 On a periscopic camera obscura and microscope *Philosophical Transactions*.

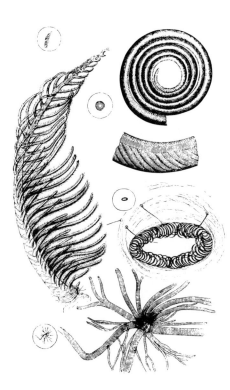

Silk-worm moth. A reproduction from *The Microscope* by Jabez Hogg (1854). The introduction to the book refers to Mr J G Kelly for '... making drawings of the objects from the Microscope and camera lucida'.

Wollaston

Wollaston's prism was used throughout the nineteenth century in spite of the difficulties already mentioned. In the body of literature searched for this chapter, the Wollaston prism was mentioned far more frequently than any other camera lucida. There was criticism, but no more than of other models. The drawings made with it were correctly orientated, though the microscope had to be in a horizontal position. This was unsuitable for specimens in water, a favourite subject, especially for the many amateur scientists in the nineteenth century. When drawing with the prism the eye had to look vertically downwards which was uncomfortable, and space for a large drawing on the table was limited by the microscope foot extending back. Almost every reference to Wollaston's prism insists on the eye being kept steadfastly in one position lest the image of the pencil be lost. Hogg (1854) after describing how to set up the microscope, prism and drawing paper, wrote 'However easy this may appear in description, it will be found very difficult in practice, and the observer must not be foiled in his first attempts but must perservere until he accomplishes his purposes.'[5] We found only the instrument maker Ross (1848) associated with adapting Wollaston's prism to the microscope; however, by the end of the century many manufacturers listed the prism as an accessory.[6]

Amici

It has already been stated that Amici designed a camera lucida which avoided the split-pupil effect of Wollaston's prism. In fact his camera lucidas appear to be

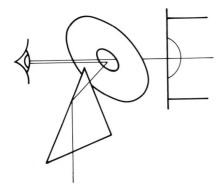

Amici's camera lucida for a horizontal microscope. Redrawn from D Lardner's book *Museum of Science and Art* (1855). The original caption said, 'The prism is interposed in this case to render the image of the hand and pencil erect'.

---

based upon designs in Wollaston's patent, which were not adopted by him for manufacture. No mention has been discovered of Amici adapting to the microscope any of his glass plates or prism and plate camera lucidas. If they were ever tried it is likely he found them unsuitable because in use the eye would be so far removed from the eye lens of the eyepiece that only a very small angle of view would result. In 1819 Amici fitted a vertical slit diaphragm to one of his designs, which presumably helped to retain the eye along one axis of the camera lucida.[3] However, he said that it did not correct the faults of ordinary camera lucidas (presumably Wollaston's) which because of their wide field of view made them suitable for use as a micrometer when adapted to microscopes and telescopes, he concluded '...which I propose to look into on another occasion'. This comment seems to confirm that his own camera lucidas, when fitted to a microscope, narrowed the angle of view through the eyepiece. The use of a camera lucida as an inexpensive micrometer will be mentioned later (see p. 153). In the following year, 1820, a paper on a reflecting microscope by Amici referred to a camera lucida adaption, but although it is illustrated it is not clear how it worked.[3] The diagram is different from any of his 1819 designs; a contemporary translation in the *Edinburgh Philosophical Journal* (1820) commented 'We must not omit to mention, that Professor Amici has contrived, by a very ingenious arrangement, to convert his microscope into a species of camera lucida, in order to enable the observer conveniently and very exactly to delineate the object, in any degree of magnitude, at pleasure.'[7]

It appears that Amici later made a complete change of design in favour of a reflector type of camera lucida for use with a horizontal microscope. Lardner (1855) wrote 'In some forms of the instrument [the camera lucida], the observer looks at the object through a small hole made in a plane reflector, placed at an angle of 45° in the direction of the paper . . . this is the form of camera lucida applied to the microscope by Professor Amici.'[8] Drawing with this device would, initially, have been difficult because of the reversal of the pencil movement in the mirror. Furthermore the drawing would be reversed, and it should be noted that the hole had to be smaller than the pupil of the eye which is about 2.8 mm diameter.[1] As with Wollaston's prism, the eye had to be kept steadily in line with the hole and the eyepiece lens in order to see the object and the reflected drawing at the same time. A few pages later Lardner described a modification to this camera lucida in which a right-angle prism is placed just below the aperture of the reflector, but he did not associate any name with the description. However, two years later, Carpenter (1857) referred to a camera lucida as 'a combination devised by M. Ch. Chevalier, of a perforated steel mirror, invented by Amici, with a reflecting prism.'[9] By this arrangement the drawing was correctly orientated because it had been reflected twice, once by the prism and again by the reflector, but still the microscope had to remain in a horizontal position. From that time onwards the instrument is always referred to as Chevalier's adaption. It is quite likely that Amici was more interested in his optical and biological research and did not consider it worthwhile pursuing the camera lucida project, which he left for Chevalier to develop.

Soemmering

In view of today's economic trends in industry it is amusing to consider that the central portion of Amici's disc, which would have been thrown away, was 'picked up' by Dr Soemmering and in turn made into a camera lucida. In fact that is all it was, a very small (less than 2.8 mm diameter) highly polished steel disc suspended a short distance from the eyepiece.† Nevertheless it was very popular and remained in production until well into the twentieth century. The centre of the eye observed the object in the mirror whilst the peripheral portion of the eye viewed the paper and pencil beyond. The drawing was reversed and the microscope had to be horizontal. Carpenter (1856) said that some microscope delineators preferred it to the camera lucida (presumably Wollaston's).[9] 'The fact is, however, that there is a sort of 'knack' in the use of each instrument.'

Glass Plates

Throughout the nineteenth century the construction of a camera lucida consisting of one or two pieces of flat glass in some form or other appears to have been a popular occupation. In 1839 the *Penny Cyclopaedia* said 'For drawing images presented by the microscope the best apparatus consists of a mirror composed of a thin piece of rather dark-coloured glass cemented to a piece of plate glass inclined at an angle of 45° in front of the eye glass.'[10] The dark-coloured glass, sometimes referred to as Muscovy glass‡, reduced the effect of a secondary reflection. A single piece of ordinary tinted glass was used in later models. This is the 'neutral tint' camera lucida which was widely used and manufactured throughout the century. As the years went by a subtle change of name took place. Beale (1857) in his first edition referred to a 'neutral tint' camera lucida; Lankester (1859) said 'Dr. Beale strongly recommends the neutral lens glass reflector.'[11,12] Carpenter (1857) also said it was recommended by Beale, but in his 1891 edition he said 'Dr. Beale devised one of the simplest

†The Royal Scottish Museum, Edinburgh, has a Soemmering camera lucida, Inventory no 1979.59.

‡Muscovite—a form of mica frequently found coloured.

121

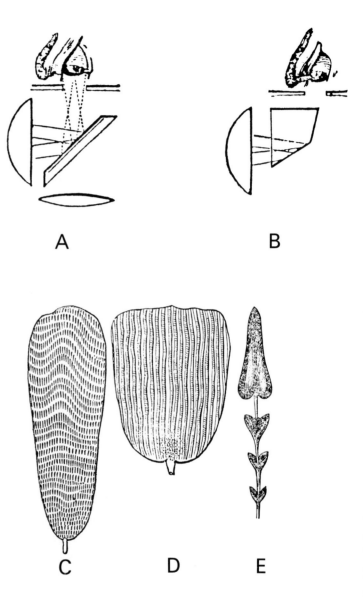

A   B

C   D   E

The *Penny Cyclopaedia* of 1839 referred to diagram A as the best apparatus for drawing images presented by the microscope, and it said that Wollaston's prism, B, is sometimes attached to the eyepiece of the microscope for the same purpose. C: a scale of *Podura plumbea*, the skiptail insect. D: a scale or feather of the *Menelaus* butterfly. E: a hair from a larva of *Dermestes sp*. These may be the first published drawings made with a camera lucida and a microscope.

Nerve fibres of the little green tree frog, *Hyla arborea*. This drawing is signed 'L.S.B. 1863', it is quite likely that it was made by Beale with the aid of his neutral tint camera lucida. From L S Beale 1880 *How to Work with the Microscope*.

cameras.'[9] This statement was repeated by Carpenter in 1901 and 'Beale's neutral tint' or 'Beale's camera lucida' remained the common names in future catalogues. No doubt it was extremely easy to use, for the eye was not presented with any image fusion problem, but the drawing was reversed and the microscope had to be horizontal. Suffolk (1870) suggested correcting the image by placing a right-angle prism between the eyepiece and the neutral glass.[13] This was an extremely ingenious and compact solution, but still the microscope had to be horizontal. However, in 1889, Ashe, at a meeting of the Quekett Microscopical Club, presented another solution which he subsequently improved.[14]

Left: the neutral tint, or Beale, camera lucida made by Messrs Bausch and Lomb. From the *Journal of the Royal Microscopical Society* (1883). Right: a neutral tint camera lucida in which a prism was incorporated. As a result of the double reflection a correct drawing was made, though the drawing board had to be tilted in order to avoid distortion. Made by Messrs Swift and illustrated in the *Journal of the Royal Microscopical Society* (1879).

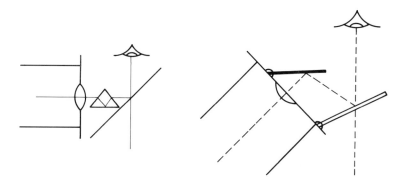

Left: a modification of the Beale or neutral tint camera lucida in order to make a correct drawing. This diagram has been drawn from W T Suffolk's description in his book *Microscopical Manipulation* (1870). The prism may have been inverted as in an early camera lucida by Amici. Right: A Ashe made this modification of the neutral tint camera lucida in order to produce a correct drawing. The microscope image is reflected by a mirror to a neutral tint glass, both are adjustable thereby allowing the microscope to be used at any angle. Redrawn from Scourfield D J 1898–1900 *Journal of the Quekett Microscopical Club*.

Ashe hinged a mirror on the flange face of an eyepiece and diagonally opposite a neutral tint glass was also hinged. The microscope rays were reflected by the mirror to the neutral tint glass thus correcting the image. The hinges allowed the microscope to be inclined at almost any position. Nelson (1895) also devised a correction for the neutral tint or Beale's camera lucida, but it was for a horizontal microscope and not so neat and compact as Ashe's arrangement.[15] Douglas (1880) used clear glass plates, and a glass with a thin transparent coating of silver in place of the neutral tint glass.[16] He also suggested using two glasses, one of which was fully silvered. Douglas obtained a correct drawing, and his illustration shows a vertical microscope. Some ten years earlier (January 1868) Professor G Govi of the University at Rome wrote, 'For a long time I had been thinking of a simple method of making a camera lucida which, free from the inconvenience of the camera lucidas of Wollaston ...and others, would lend itself with ease, and not too much expense. . . Now I seem to have resolved the problem. . .'. Govi's solution was '. . . a flat thin sheet of glass, with a face covered in a very fine layer of gold, silver or platinum. . . In this way it has a most vivid appearance by reflexion and vivid enough by trans- mission to avoid double images and it doesn't halve the pupil of the eye.'[17] In November of the same year, 1868, Govi presented to the Academy of Sciences, Turin, two camera lucidas of his design constructed by Guiseppe Poggiali of Florence. No further reference to this type of camera lucida has been discovered. How- ever, Professor Govi continued his researches and, as we shall read later, he made an important step in camera lucida design. Aylward (1883) used only a thin cover glass as a reflector at the eyepiece.[18] A very thin glass does have a minimal secondary reflection but the drawing would have been reversed and the microscope was horizontal. The most important contribution to this class of camera lucida for use with a vertical microscope was made by Burch in 1878.[19] Curiously, he devised it for micrometry, not for drawing, yet he referred to it as 'like a camera lucida set backwards'. In principle Burch's apparatus pre-empts Abbé, whose camera lucida was produced three years later and is still used in some laboratories. Burch mounted a piece of mirror with a small central hole (less than 2.8 mm) at 45° over the eyepiece of a vertical microscope. On an arm extending away from the microscope body he arranged a slide holding a scale. The scale was reflected by the eyepiece mirror and through the hole in the mirror he was able to observe the object. The two images were fused in the brain and he was able to make a measurement. However, there was only one reflection and he pointed out that 'the scale should be numbered with the figures reversed'. By placing a stage micr- ometer in the microscope Burch was able to slide the scale along the arm until the graduations matched, thus calibrating the position of the scale for the objective and eyepiece in use.

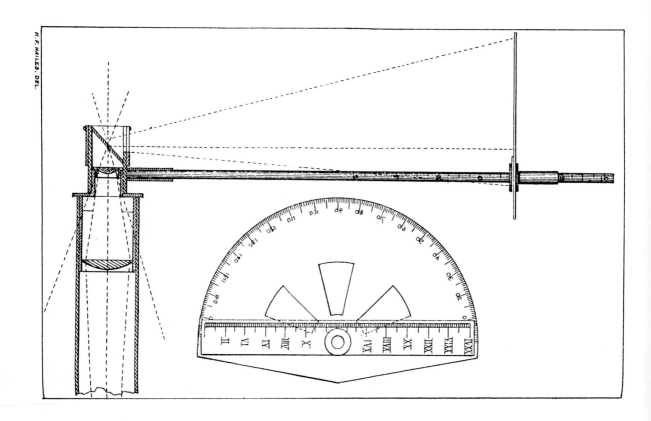

A micrometer devised by G J Burch who referred to it as 'an inverse application of the camera lucida'. From the *Journal of the Quekett Microscopical Club* (1878).

Nachet

Carpenter (1857) said that M M Nachet had recently devised a camera lucida consisting of a rhomboid prism with a small prism attached.[9] It was mounted on a vertical microscope and the drawing was reflected from one end of the rhomboid to the other where it was seen by the eye. A very small cylindrical prism cemented to the eye face of the rhomboid allowed the microscope object to be seen. A Mr P Gray of Camden Town, London, writing in 1860, objected to this arrangement because the microscope was too tall for vertical viewing, furthermore he appeared to have misunderstood the drawing of Nachet's camera lucida in Carpenter and he disapproved of the rhomboid prism and suggested it be replaced by a right-angle prism with a hole drilled through it...and so on.[20] M Nachet, Jun, replied with patience though he did remark that Gray's objections arose 'from his not having employed it' (i.e. the camera lucida).[21] Nachet concluded his reply by describing a new rhomboid camera lucida which allowed the use of an inclined microscope; Carpenter (1862, 1875) referred to both models by M M Nachet. The *Journal of the Royal Microscopical Society* (1882) announced an improved camera lucida by Nachet in which 'M. Nachet has made use of a suggestion of Professor Govi, and deposits a thin film of gold on the face of the prism.'[22] The thin film was reflective and transparent, consequently there was no longer the problem of centring the eye over the small prism as with the earlier model. In 1886 the same journal referred to a rhomboid prism for use with an inclined microscope which also had Govi's thin gold layer.[23] The announcement said that it 'is now made by M. A. Nachet'. In the same volume appeared a note from M L Malassez who suggested altering the prism of a Nachet camera lucida in such a way that the microscope may be inclined without causing distortion in the drawing.[24] A Nachet/Govi camera lucida made by Koristka of Milan was announced in the *Journal of the*

A

B

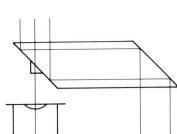
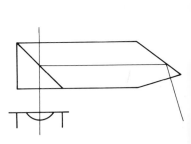

Nachet's camera lucida. The complete apparatus is shown on the left. The central diagram shows his first model (split pupil) in which a very small cylindrical prism allowed observation of the microscope image, in effect an 'optical hole'. The drawing made with this camera lucida was not distorted but it was not possible to make a large drawing because of the proximity of the microscope.

The diagram on the right illustrates the improved see-through model (*c.*1875) incorporating Govi's suggestion of a thin layer of gold between the large prism and the rhomboid, which was reshaped in order to extend the drawing area away from the microscope. However, this required a tilted drawing board to avoid distortion. Redrawn from the *Journal of the Royal Microscopical Society* (1882).

Royal Microscopical Society 1894.[25] Carpenter (1901) does not mention Nachet. However, a Nachet catalogue of 1900 lists a Nachet/Govi camera lucida fitted with a filter for reducing the glare of the drawing paper.[26] Also listed are two models of a simple, single-lens microscope, each fitted with a prism and a mirror on an extended arm. There is no description of the prism.

Abbe

A camera lucida designed by Professor Ernest Abbe was reported in the *Journal of the Royal Microscopical*

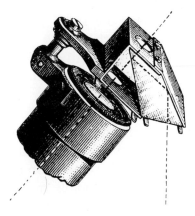

Nachet's rhomboidal camera lucida for use with an inclined microscope. This illustration also shows Govi's gilded right-angle prism. From the *Journal of the Royal Microscopical Society* (1886).

A simple, single-lens microscope complete with a camera lucida. From a Nachet catalogue of 1892.

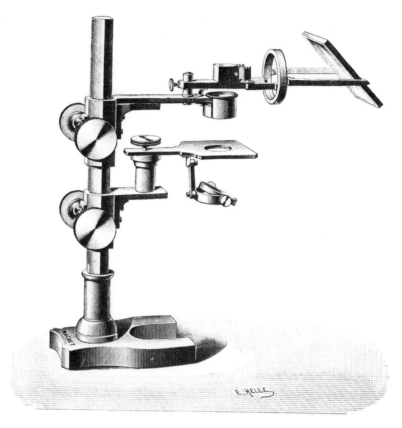

Society of 1882, unfortunately with an incorrect diagram.[27] The instrument consisted of a right-angle prism with a fully silvered hypotenuse except for a central clear portion less than 2.8 mm diameter. The silvering was protected by another right-angle prism cemented to it. The resulting cube was placed centrally over the eyepiece enabling direct observation of the object through the clear portion of the cube. An arm extending from the microscope body carried a mirror set at 45° which reflected the drawing paper to the cube where it was reflected and seen by the periphery of the eye pupil. Abbe's camera lucida satisfied the requirements for an undistorted and correctly orientated drawing made with a vertical microscope, or at any inclination provided the drawing board was parallel with the microscope stage. In use it was as easy, or

129

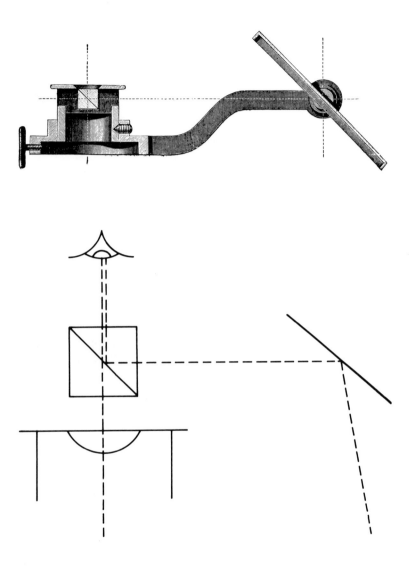

Professor Ernst Abbe's camera lucida. This instrument was extremely popular, and although its manufacture is now discontinued many are still used, particularly by workers with monocular microscopes. The lower diagram is redrawn from the incorrect publication of 1882, the ray from the drawing board should be parallel with that of the microscope as in the top illustration of 1883. From the *Journal of the Royal Microscopical Society* (1882, 1883).

130

difficult, as Amici's original perforated disc or Soemmering's little disc. The ray diagram in the 1882 *Journal* is incorrect because Abbe intended the microscope optical axis and the drawing axis to be parallel. A correct illustration, together with a fuller explanation of the instrument, was printed in the *Journal* the following year, 1883.[28] Except for the later addition of filters to balance the illumination of the microscope and the drawing images, Abbe's camera lucida has retained its principle and appearance throughout the years to the present time. Many research workers still use this type of camera lucida.

It is fitting to refer to Burch (1878), as Carpenter (1901) did, and point out that whilst the two pieces of apparatus are similar, Burch, it would appear, did not see his as an improved camera lucida.[19,9] Presumably it required the wider vision of Abbe to devise a simple but correct instrument from the great variety of camera lucidas devised or suggested in the literature. In view of the long history of Abbe's instrument in microscopy it is amusing to read a comment by Anthony (1884) 'I may say, that while not appreciating the Abbe prism used for the purpose for which it was constructed, I recognised a most valuable quality which it possesses, for copying drawings and engravings of small area, either of the size of the original or with slight magnification at will. I think I can see a considerable future for this prism in certain branches of the fine arts.'[29]

The Cube

From receiving hardly any notice in microscopy for about half a century the semi-reflecting cube has today become almost the only camera lucida used with the microscope. The cube is made of two right-angle prisms cemented at their hypotenuse, with a thin transparent layer of silver between.

After experimenting with plates of glass and rhomboidal prisms coated with a thin layer of metal, Professor G Govi finally modified a Nachet camera lucida. Although a modification it was in fact a new form of camera lucida, Govi's account of his work was read to the French Academy of Sciences in 1874 by Mr Ch Robin.[30]

Govi coated the hypotenuse of a right-angle prism with a very thin layer of gold (only 10 to 15 molecules thick) and cemented it to the eyepiece face of Nachet's rhomboidal prism, in place of the latter's very small prism. The thin semi-transparent layer of metal, not unlike certain present day sunglasses, transmitted the microscope image and at the same time reflected the drawing from the opposite face of the rhomboid. The two images were completely superimposed, and as the eye no longer had to be steadfastly held in one position the problem of fusing two separate images in the mind was removed. Govi noted that his camera lucida, to be made by Nachet, was suitable for drawing with the microscope, drawing with a magnifying glass, that is at low magnifications, and for drawing natural history subjects and landscapes. He pointed out that the gold layer tinted the microscope image emerald green and the drawing paper yellow.

We are now aware that Govi had produced the ideal camera lucida for the microscope, certainly in principle. There was the minor problem of the tinted image. For landscape work there was the somewhat greater problem of an inverted, and consequently reversed, image; some means of providing a second reflection was required. However, no further development took place. The device remained with Nachet who continued to use it with his rhomboidal prism camera lucida, and, as far as can be ascertained, made this type of camera lucida until the 1930s.

At a meeting of the Royal Microscopical Society in 1898 the President called upon a Mr Swift to describe a new camera lucida and a new monochromat screen (filter).[31] Swift said that as the inventor, F E Ives, was

Swift–Ives camera lucida, from a
Swift catalogue of 1899.

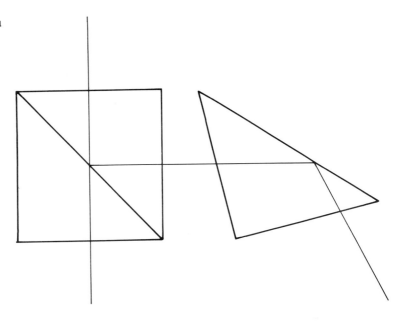

in the room he would ask him to describe them. Ives
was an American, and as a self-styled amateur inventor
was one of the pioneers of three-colour photography.
He said he had taken a camera lucida from Swift's
showcase and dismantled it. His description suggests
that it was a Swift–Abbe instrument. He removed the
heavy silvering and replaced it with a very thin,
semi-transparent layer of silver; he then re-cemented
the two prisms to make a cube which would transmit
and reflect. The silver did not produce the colour cast
associated with the gold film of Govi's instrument. In
effect he had done no more than Govi nearly a quarter
of a century earlier. It is interesting to note that, in the
discussion which followed, Conrad Beck said he
thought a similar device which had a very thin silvering
between two prisms had been made some years previously by Zeiss. A footnote in the *Journal* says 'Since
the meeting Mr. Beck has written to say that the
camera referred to was made by Nachet, and had
gilding instead of silvering.'

In recent years, and probably since 1925 or so, the
semi-reflecting silvered cube of Ives has been known,

133

familiarly, as a 'Swan' cube. Many people in the microscope and allied optical fields still use this term but when questioned about its origin they have nothing to offer. However, it appears that the name 'Swan' has been well known in photometry since about 1890 and, as that science and microscopy tended to use similar optical arrangements, the name was freely used for beam-splitting devices in the form of a cube.

William Swan (1818–94), a professor at St Andrew's University, Scotland, was interested in the composition of flames, and, in 1859, in order to further these studies he designed a photometer.[32] The comparator of his apparatus consisted of two right-angle prisms cemented by a very small drop of Canada balsam in the centre of their hypotenuse, this provided central transmission with a peripheral area of reflection.

In 1889 O Lummer and E Brodhun devised a photometer in which they used a right-angle prism with a convex cylindrical hypotenuse in close contact with the plane hypotenuse of another right-angle prism.[33] This cube provided a narrow central strip of transmission with an area of reflection on each side. Most of the literature on photometry associates Swan with Lummer–Brodhun, as for instance: 'William Swan's prism photometer . . . is fundamentally the same as that described by O. Lummer and E. Brodhun . . .';[34] 'This [the Lummer–Brodhun cube] was first used by W. Swan and described by him some thirty years before its introduction by Lummer and Brodhun.';[35] and 'Swan Cube. The prism system employed in the Lummer–Brodhun or Swan photometer.'[36]

A satisfactory explanation for this relationship is given by R A Houstoun in his *Treatise of Light* (1915, 1927) where he said 'This photometer although usually accredited to Lummer and Brodhun was nevertheless invented very much earlier by Swan. But as there was no need for accurate photometry in his time, it was forgotten, and not brought into use until invented independently by Lummer and Brodhun.'[37]

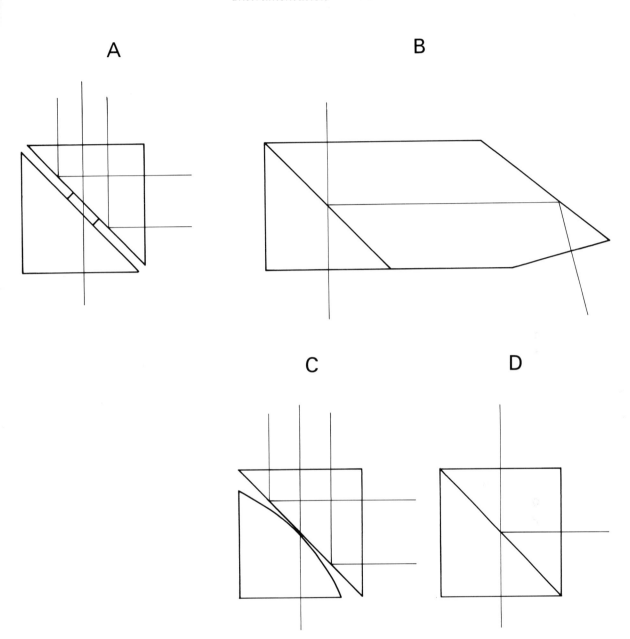

Beam-splitting prisms. A: Swan's Canada balsam cube for photometry, 1859. B: Govi's thin layer of gold modification of Nachet's camera lucida, 1874. C: Lummer and Brudhon contact cube for photometry, 1889. D: Ives' thin layer of silver cube which he adapted to a Swift camera lucida, 1898.

135

We might leave the photometer aspect of the cube at that point, though there may be some interest in a slight abberation. R S Clay in his *Treatise on Practical Light* (1911) referred to 'The Swan, or Lummer and Brodhun Photometer' and in the description said 'The hypotenuse [of one right-angle prism] is first silvered, and then the silver is removed over some portion... The two prisms are then cemented together with Canada balsam....'[38] Clay has described Abbe's camera lucida prism.

S Bradbury, in his book *Evolution of the Microscope* (1967), said 'The first really high power (binocular microscope) system was introduced by Conrad Beck in 1913. It owed its inspiration to an invention by F E Ives in America in 1902 and used the so-called 'Swan cube' as a beam splitting device.'[39]

This, and the previous quotations, appears to be the best evidence for the semi-reflecting cube being called a 'Swan cube'. That Ives' cube, as such, did not flourish at the time is probably due to prejudice among microscopists who preferred to use conventional and established instruments, as is reflected in the manufacturers' catalogues—also, perhaps, because Ives was relatively unknown in the microscope field and, as he himself wrote, was 'an amateur inventor'.

To conclude this diversion on the semi-reflecting cube a brief mention should be made of another Swan, though it is doubtful whether his name was ever associated with the cube prism. Henry Swan (no relation of William) of London was interested in stereoscopy and took out patents for methods of mounting a pair of stereoscopic photographs in such a manner that they could be viewed without any optical aid.[40] The photographs were each mounted behind wedge-shaped prisms which were arranged with a slight air gap between them. The 'Casket Miniature' was an interesting experiment in auto-stereoscopy but it soon disappeared from the market. However, a specimen may be seen at the Science Museum, South Kensington.

136

Prisms and Mirrors

Had W S Gilbert read the journals of the Royal Microscopical Society and the Quekett Microscopical Club he might have remarked, 'A positive plethora of prisms and not a prune to the purpose.' No fewer than eighteen varieties of this type of camera lucida were discovered in the literature. By 1880 the microscope was nearing the peak of its technical development yet a great deal of the progress had been achieved by individuals and the comparatively small firms which had grown up in the tradition of the eighteenth-century instrument maker. There were considerable contributions from amateur microscopists/inventors who, with a private competence, were able to commission an optician or mechanic to carry out their notions, however impractical they may have been commercially. Many of the camera lucidas reflect this situation, for instance the instrument of Russell (1879) and Oberhauser (1882) would hardly have been suitable for large-scale production.[41,42] Some of the comments in the journals, whilst amusing, suggest that a few of the camera lucidas were made as a result of a whimsical idea. An example is that of Hofmann, in which three reflecting surfaces produced a reversed drawing. The secretary of the Royal Microscopical Society contributed a paper to the Society's *Journal* (1879), 'On some recent forms of Camera Lucida', in which he briefly described Hofmann's design and obviously could not resist quoting from the latter's letter, 'The camera supresses all existing eyepieces.'[43] In 1882 the same journal reported 'Dr. Cramer can only concur to a small extent in the warm praise which Dr. H. von

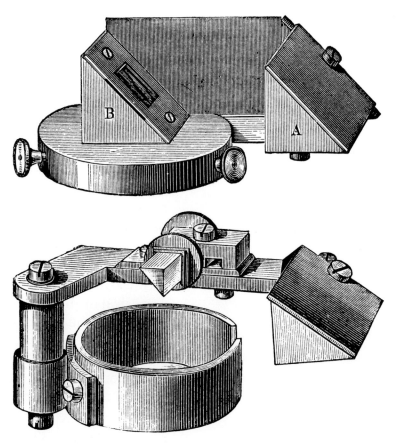

Top: The camera lucida of Nobert. Bottom: The camera lucida of Doyere and Milne-Edwards. The description accompanying these illustrations is one of the rare occasions when the plural *camerae lucidae* appears in the literature. From the *Journal of the Royal Microscopical Society* (1883).

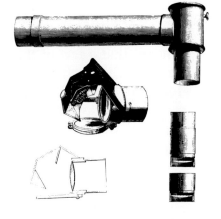

Dr D T Hofmann's camera lucida. From the *Journal of the Royal Microscopical Society* (1879).

Heurck has bestowed upon Hofmann's camera lucida.'[42] And again in 1883 under the heading 'Camerae Lucidae of Nobert and of Doyere and Milne-Edwards'† the editor of the *Journal of the Royal Microscopical Society* commented 'We describe and

†The Polytechnic Museum, Moscow, has a camera lucida made by F A Nobert (1806–81). This instrument maker is better known for his dividing engine, which was capable of ruling lines about 0.12 mm apart.

Chevalier's adaptation of Amici's camera lucida. Amici's original perforated disc at 45° over the eyepiece is just visible in this illustration. From the *Journal of the Royal Microscopical Society* (1883).

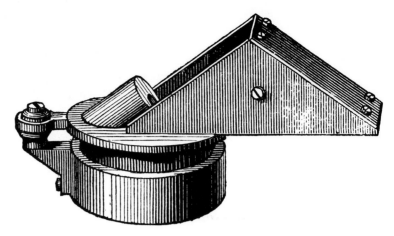

illustrate these forms more as a 'contribution to the history of the camera lucida than as offering any novelty at the present day'.[44]

Chevalier (1883) increased the size of the prism in his adaption of Amici's perforated reflector, thereby making the camera lucida suitable for a vertical microscope.[45] Grunow (1883) replaced the mirror of Abbe's camera lucida with a prism set very close to the cemented cube, consequently the drawing was distorted.[46] Distortion arose because the light rays from the drawing were not parallel with those of the microscope as in Abbe's instrument. By tilting the drawing board surface to a right angle to the prism axis distortion was eliminated. Grunow's prism was mounted on a pivot which allowed the microscope to be used upright or inclined. When used in an inclined position it would have been possible to make an undistorted drawing on the table in front of the microscope by suitably adjusting the angle of the prism.

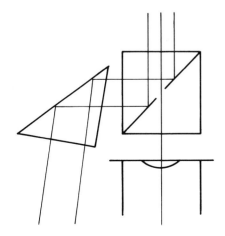

J Grunow's camera lucida in which the mirror of Abbe's camera lucida was replaced by a totally reflecting prism. Redrawn from the *American Monthly Microscopical Journal* (1882) (also the *Journal of the Royal Microscopical Society* (1883)).

Seibert and Krafft (1883) made an attractive-looking camera lucida in which they reproduced the effect of Nachet's rhomboid by using two mirrors.[47] Schroeder (1883) designed a camera lucida for use with the microscope inclined at 45° which produced a correct and undistorted drawing.[48] It consisted of a rhomboidal prism with a right-angle prism adjacent to the eyepiece face of the rhomboid. The slight air gap and the selection of suitable angles for the rhomboid produced the same effect as the Nachet–Govi instrument. The microscope image and the drawing paper were superimposed. Schroeder's camera lucida was made for him by the firm of Andrew Ross.

These examples are sufficient to indicate the variety of camera lucidas which were manufactured or individually constructed during the last century. Perhaps it is appropriate to end with reference to a home-made design by Dr C Cramer (1882).[42] By way of introduction he said, 'Those who use the microscope, especially beginners, are not always in a position to buy a camera

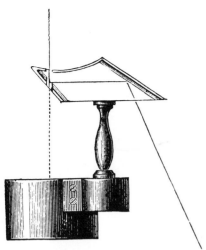

Seibert and Krafft's camera lucida. This is an extremely simple construction in which mirrors were used in place of a rhomboid prism. The microscope image was observed through a hole in the eyepiece mirror. From the *Journal of the Royal Microscopical Society* (1883).

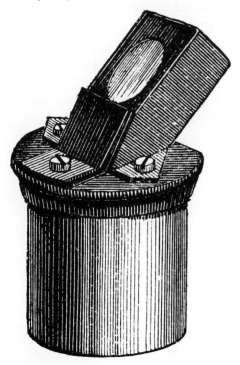

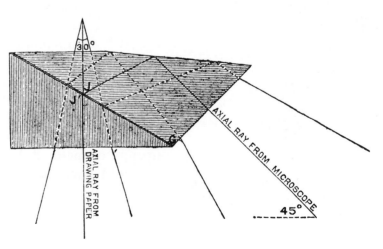

A camera lucida designed by Dr Hugo Schroeder for a microscope inclined at 45°. It was made to his drawings by Messrs Ross. From the *Journal of the Royal Microscopical Society* (1883) (also Carpenter (1901)).

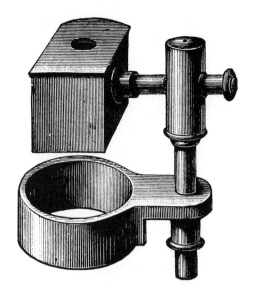

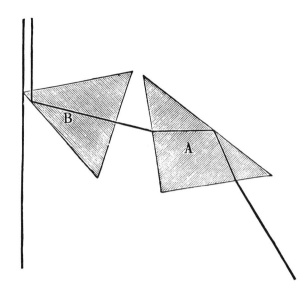

A Zeiss camera lucida of the split-pupil type for use with a vertical microscope. From a Zeiss catalogue of 1898.

lucida. I think therefore, that I shall be doing many a service by showing how any one who possesses a little mechanical dexterity may make for himself a very serviceable camera lucida.'

A home-made camera lucida. Dr C Cramer gave full instructions for making this simple camera lucida in the *Journal of the Royal Microscopical Society* (1882).

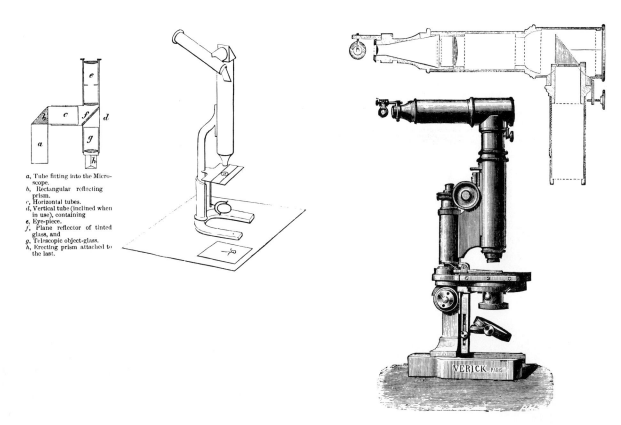

a, Tube fitting into the Microscope.
b, Rectangular reflecting prism.
c, Horizontal tubes.
d, Vertical tube (inclined when in use), containing
e, Eye-piece.
f, Plane reflector of tinted glass, and
g, Telescopic object-glass.
h, Erecting prism attached to the last.

Left: this camera lucida, designed by J Cunningham Russell, provided an undistorted drawing from a vertical microscope yet gave the user the comfort of an inclined eyepiece. From the *Journal of the Royal Microscopical Society* (1879).

Right: Oberhauser's camera lucida made by E Hartnack of Potsdam. 'Verick, Paris' is probably the name of a retailer. From the *Journal of the Royal Microscopical Society* (1882).

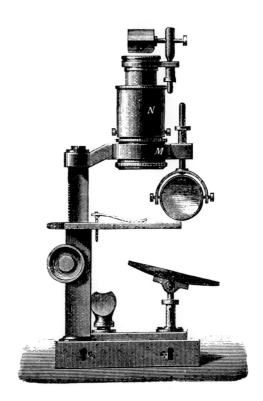

Left: this apparatus, made by Winkel, was used for drawing objects at low magnification on the left of the stand, and at natural size at the right. From the *Journal of the Royal Microscopical Society* (1884).

Right: a low-power microscope complete with a Zeiss type of camera lucida made by H Jung. The Brucke compound lens gave continuous magnification of about 1–20 and 4–30 without having to move the camera lucida. From the *Journal of the Royal Microscopical Society* (1884).

Distortion. When an eyepiece camera lucida is used it is necessary to have a tilted drawing board in order to avoid distortion. The diagram shows an elongation of the right-hand portion of a drawing made on the table; a drawing board at right angles to the prism axis would make a true drawing.

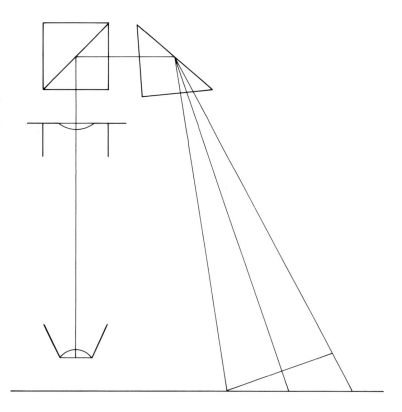

Drawing and the Microscope

In recent times picture books of microscopic subjects have been produced with very little text and are frequently devoid of any scientific content. Many such books are merely decorative, produced for the pleasure of the publisher and reader; however, some are published as pattern books for artists and designers. Many microscopists of the last century were more than aware of the beautiful forms revealed by the microscope and were at great pains to make drawings and paintings which would express those wonders of creation. Apart from the very full aesthetic appreciation of their subjects, microscopists were frequently urged to draw, if not all, then certainly any new specimens discovered during their investigations. The first paragraph of Beale (1868) on drawing microscopic subjects is as relevant today as it was then.

OF DRAWING OBJECTS—It may be truly said that no real advance in our knowledge of the minute structure of animal or vegetable tissue, can be communicated to others, unless accurate drawings are made, for it is almost hopeless for an observer to attempt to describe what he sees in words, and such descriptions, however careful they may be, scarcely admit of comparison with those of other persons. On the other hand, a truthful drawing of what a man has seen recently, may be compared with drawings which may be made a hundred years hence, and although the means of observation will be far more perfect than they are at present, such comparisons may be useful in many ways, and especially in preventing erroneous conclusions. By description alone ingenious persons who take pains may so express themselves as to render it very doubtful what their opinion really is, but if they can only be persuaded to make a drawing, there can be no doubt concerning the exact nature of their view. I think that an honest enquirer cannot be of greater use in his time than by making good drawings of what he has seen, and we may feel sure that those who follow us will respect our drawings, if honest copies of nature, although very little of what is now written will be read some years hence, when the whole aspect of our department of science shall be changed.

Suffolk, in his 1869 paper to the Quekett Microscopical Club, emphasised the importance of observers making their own drawings; he said '... but I think almost any microscopist might be able, with the aid of some one or other of the instruments I am about to describe, to make useful records of his own observations—rough, possibly in execution, but still much more truthful than drawings made by a more skilful but less scientific artist'.[49]

It has been noted, however, that the camera lucida as a drawing aid was not completely without criticism and there are a few comments similar to those made by Draper in 1883, 'No drawings can be greatly advanced by the camera lucida. The latter can be used for quickly and accurately fixing and drawing the salient points, but any attempt at elaborate detail will end in confusion, and useful as it is in the earliest steps, it should be discarded as soon as possible.'[50] Draper made this remark when he exhibited his drawings and paintings from the microscope at a Conversazione of the Royal Microscopical Society. He described his technique, stating that he made some of his paintings within a $3\frac{3}{4}$ inch circle with a black surround in order to give the impression of the 'field with a B eyepiece'. Hardy (1884) preferred to make his drawings directly on black paper in Chinese white with a fine sable brush, commenting that drawings made in this manner had the expression of character in contradistinction to a mere copy or outline.[51] Anthony (1884) described how he

146

made an extra large drawing; whilst not new his method is amusing (the method had been mentioned by Quekett in 1848).[29,6]

> ... the microscope was well raised over the edge of the table. The image—enormously magnified—got from a 1/6 objective, was projected by the prism, and was traced upon the paper by the aid of a pencil; which pencil might be said to be 5 feet long, inasmuch as it was formed by a crayon tied firmly on a joint of a fishing rod. That the outline so traced was a bit 'shaky', and needed 'mending' may well be imagined, but the reparation has, I think, not been made at the expense of the characteristic curves of the various diatoms.

The image was not, in fact, 'projected'. This is yet another instance of the confused use of words in respect of the camera lucida and the camera obscura. If the image had been projected he need not have used a long pencil, but simply got down on the floor and traced the image.

Piersol's contribution to the Royal Microscopical Society's *Journal* (1888) on photographs and drawings described his method of making 'an elaborately finished drawing' by working with pen and pencil on an under-exposed photographic print.[52] Of more interest, perhaps, is his comment that he 'had occasion recently to use the Abbe prism to sketch some 1400 sections...'. Unfortunately this is the only reference which mentions the number of drawings made. There appears nothing unusual about the statement, Piersol merely mentioning it in connection with a screen he devised for adjusting the lamp-light on his drawing paper. Balanced illumination of the microscope and drawing paper is important when using a camera lucida, and it was frequently mentioned in the journals. Goethart (1894) and Andrews (1898) suggested that tinted papers would help to make the drawing and pencil more easily discerned in the camera lucida; for the same reason Creteur (1882) recommended drawing with a metal point on gelatine.[53,54,55]

A fully adjustable and calibrated drawing table which was illustrated in the catalogues of Reichert and Zeiss at the end of the nineteenth century. From the catalogues of Zeiss (1898, 1934) and Reichert (1909).

The journals have their lighter moments. The problem of keeping the eye steadfastly in one position over the prism was solved in 1879 by T.R.I.[56] Writing from his vicarage at Codicote he suggested that two uprights with a padded crossbar be clamped to the table over the microscope. The padded bar was for resting the forehead. In the same year Professor Malassez suggested an improvement in the mounting of camera lucidas, noting that manufacturers 'always place this joint at the side, so that the draughtsman cannot avoid knocking (his nose) against it, or else be obliged to give a very fatiguing inclination to the head. This inconvenience may be avoided by placing the joint not at the side, but at the anterior part of the camera.'[57]

Further Aids for Drawing with the Microscope

In spite of the great variety of camera lucidas which were devised for the microscope in the last century not all microscopists adopted it for their drawings. Benjamin Martin's glass disc ruled in squares has already been mentioned, but it seems that it may have been

148

temporarily forgotten by microscope manufacturers because Suffolk (1870) referred to one he had made by Beck, and illustrated the method of its use.[2,13] The most unlikely drawing aid for the microscope, a pantograph, was made and described by Roberts in 1872.[58]

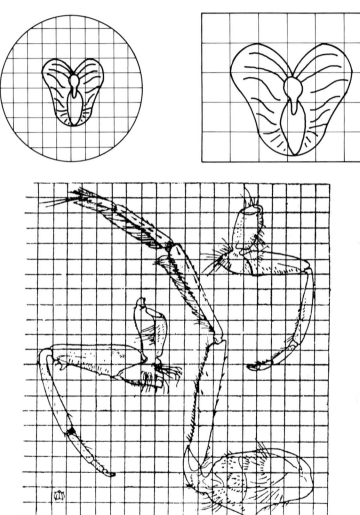

Two drawings made with the aid of a micrometer grid placed in the eyepiece of a microscope. Top: redrawn from Suffolk's *Microscopical Manipulation* (1870), illustrating the appearance of an object in an eyepiece and the drawing. Bottom: from Wallis's *Analytical Microscopy* (1957); a drawing of the legs of the water boatman, *Notonecta undulata*.

149

In place of the tracing point of a pantograph he had a sight consisting of crossed lines on a glass slide. The slide was manoeuvred in the image plane of the eyepiece through a slot in the barrel. Hilgendorf (1883) was somewhat less ambitious, he adapted a pantograph to a magnifying glass for low-power drawing.[59]

Projection or the Camera Obscura

At the time of the solar microscope, in the eighteenth century, the sun was the only illuminant brilliant enough to make a projected image for drawing. The Argand oil lamp, patented by Aime Argand in 1784, was used for the lucernal microscope. This instrument produced a projected image satisfactory for visual purposes, but it was hardly bright enough for drawing. In order to make a drawing with the lucernal microscope the image was transmitted through translucent drawing paper, not projected upon it. Even as late as 1832 a solar arrangement was described and illustrated in the *Library of Useful Knowledge*.[60] However, artificial light sources sufficiently powerful to allow projection were available in the nineteenth century, and some microscopists preferred to trace the ever-present projected image rather than cope with the sometimes disappearing virtual reflection image of the camera lucida. Hart (1866) wrote 'In all books on the microscope . . . the camera lucida has been the only form put forward . . . I don't know how others find it, but I certainly do not like either the cramped stooping position necessary for its use, nor does it contribute to accuracy of tracing. I have, therefore . . . been in the habit of using the camera obscura.'[61] A description of his apparatus followed.

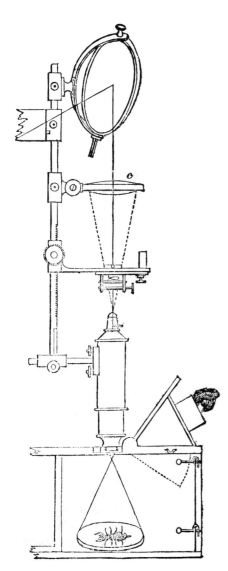

A microscope fitted with a mirror and condenser lens for solar illumination in order to project an image for observation and drawing. The front of the image box was let down to allow the image to be traced. From *The Library of Useful Knowledge, Natural Philosophy* vol. 2 (1832).

A simple projection microscope designed by Dr L Edinger for making drawings at low magnification by projection. The lower illustration shows the apparatus modified and adapted for photography by Leitz about 1895. From Grehn J 1977 *Leitz Microscopes for 125 Years.*

Piffard (1892) enumerated three methods for drawing: by careful study and drawing from memory; by one eye observing and the other drawing, 'a sort of autoprojection'; the camera lucida.[62] He was dissatisfied with all three methods and preferred to project the image by means of a right-angle prism. He continued, 'Personally I find this instrument much more convenient and satisfactory than the camera lucida. Mechanical micrograms must yield, however, to photographs;

Sir Walter Sendall's device for making accurate measurements of microscopic objects. From the *Journal of the Royal Microscopical Society*.

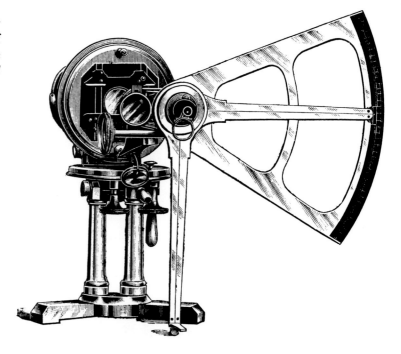

and the micrographic science of the future will seek the aid of the pencil less, and make more frequent use of the convenience and accuracy of photography.'

Apparatus for projection usually consisted of a simple right-angle prism suitably mounted for attachment to the eyepiece. Edinger (1891) described a simple microscope (single lens) consisting of a condenser, a mirror at 45°, a stage to carry the specimen and a magnifying glass below.[63] The arrangement allowed drawings to be made from 2 to 20 times magnification. Sendall's paper of the same year 'On an Improved method of making Microscopical Measurements with the Camera Lucida' is an interesting reflection of the prevailing amateur status of scientists in the last century.[64] At that time the camera lucida, camera obscura and photographic camera were widely known instruments, yet throughout the paper Sendall referred to 'a camera'. He mentioned the projection and measurement of a virtual image, which is not possible.

However, in spite of his lack of understanding of optical principles and language, Sendall solved the problem of making accurate measurements in a most elegant manner, and his apparatus made a magnificent addition to the microscope. It had the appearance of the hands of a clock fixed at right angles, with a small white tablet fixed at right angles to one hand whilst the other hand, shaped as a pointer, traversed a graduated quadrant. The hands are pivoted at the axis of the microscope. The object to be measured was positioned along the horizontal diameter of the field in the microscope, and the extremities projected on to the white tablet. First one end of the object was projected and the position of the pointer on the graduated quadrant noted; then the tablet was swung to the other end of the object to give another reading of the quadrant. As both scale readings were equidistant from the microscope axis a precise measurement was made.

Micrometer

Almost every general reference to the camera lucida mentions its use as an inexpensive micrometer. The procedure was to draw on a card, by means of a camera lucida, the divisions of a stage micrometer. When it was required to measure a microscopic object the card was placed in the drawing area of a camera lucida on the microscope. The divisions on the card were thus superimposed on the image of the object to be measured. A drawing of a stage micrometer had to be made for each combination of objective and eyepiece in use, and it was necessary to maintain the same distance from the card to the camera lucida on each occasion.

Photography

A few papers and notes on the camera lucida also refer to photography. Riddell (1854) described a method for making stereographic pairs of microscopic specimens.[65] He placed a small prism behind the objective on an axis transverse to the microscope axis. By a slight movement of the prism he obtained left- and right-hand views of which he said, '. . . a careful camera lucida drawing is to be made, or a photographic impression made'.

Piersol (1880) made an interesting comparison of the camera lucida and photography.[50] He concluded that photography was the more suitable for very low powers (20 to 70 diam.) and for very high powers (500 to 1500 diam.). He said the limitation of the plane of focus 'frequently renders photographs, under medium powers, unsatisfactory substitutes for more diagrammatic drawings'. He referred to medium powers as 1/4 or 1/6, which for our present day microscopes would be approximately the $\times 25$ and $\times 40$ objectives respectively.

In view of the progress that photomicrography was eventually to make, Suffolk's comment in his paper, 'On Some of the Means of Delineating Microscopic Objects' (1869) is amusing, and a warning to those who look askance at any new process: '. . . and the necessity of employing special apparatus and mastering a somewhat delicate set of chemical processes, will ever prevent its extensive employment'.[49]

The Twentieth Century

The end of the nineteenth century saw the close of the era of the amateur scientist. As the present century advanced science became a large and important profession of many disciplines. A fast-growing science industry developed which could afford its own instrument research engineers, with the result that in all but a few instances it was no longer necessary for scientists to devise and make their own basic apparatus. These changes in the scientific world were accelerated by the war of 1914–18, and again in the early 1940s. The World Wars created unstable economic situations which affected industry and brought about a rationalisation of production. Today there are only two forms of camera lucida for use with the microscope. During the 1920s and 1930s photography progressed rapidly and became the accepted means of recording microscopical material. The cine-camera was used extensively from about 1940 in order to study the movement and growth of micro-organisms. Since about 1960 the video camera has been adapted to the microscope, and, from the 1970s, to the image-analysing computer, resulting in a considerable decline in the use of purely photographic methods.

In spite of these precise and objective techniques some scientists, particularly in medicine and entomology, often prefer to make a drawing with the aid of a camera lucida or by means of a projected real image. A drawing provides the emphasis and clarity which is not possible by photography. There are occasions when both a photograph and a drawing are used to illustrate the same subject, especially of biological material.

It is, perhaps, significant of the changes in the

155

scientific world that only a dozen references to the camera lucida for the microscope were found in the indexes to the *Journal of the Royal Microscopical Society*, the *Journal of the Quekett Microscopical Club* and *Nature* from 1900 to 1980.[†] A large collection of microscopical catalogues at the Science Museum, South Kensington, confirmed the effect of economic and production changes during the century. As the information on camera lucidas was gathered from the catalogues it fell into four periods which approximate to the social and political changes of the past eighty years.

1900–10

The largest number of catalogues (15) was available for this period. A variety of camera lucidas and drawing boards was manufactured which appears to indicate the continuance of the stable and relatively peaceful era of the nineteenth century. The foremost camera lucidas available were those of Abbe, Wollaston and Beale. Several firms were making eyepiece camera lucidas for use with an inclined microscope. The modification of Beale's camera lucida designed by Ashe was available from Watson. Swift supplied Schroeder's camera lucida and Ives' semi-silvered cube. Beck made Soemmering's steel disc and Wollaston's prism, also Beale's neutral tint camera lucida and their own model of a drawing eyepiece. Drawing boards, simple and complex, were available from a number of firms. Leitz and Reichert listed three different boards whilst Zeiss had a range of four. A board by Reichert is particularly interesting in that it carried the complete assembly of microscope and drawing table.

[†]Besides these there were two commercial announcements and two references for projection methods.

1911–20

A war period; unfortunately only five catalogues are available. It would appear that Baker reduced their range to Beale's neutral tint and Abbe's camera lucida. Swift and Watson continued to supply the same instruments as in previous years and the latter added a large prism for projecting a real image. No doubt this was the result of an increased use of electric lamps to provide the intense illumination required for projection. Leitz produced a projection mirror for use with a horizontal microscope, a small table tent being supplied with the mirror in order to shield extraneous light and increase the image contrast. Leitz continued to supply two drawing eyepieces and two models of the Abbe camera lucida; also listed was a single-lens simple microscope with a prism and mirror for drawing at low magnifications. The only mention of a Wollaston camera lucida appeared in a Kohl (German) catalogue. No drawing boards were listed in any of the catalogues.

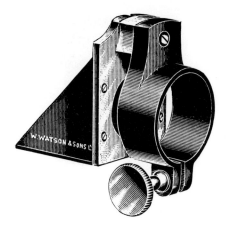

Watson's large prism which projected the microscope image directly onto a drawing board. From a Watson catalogue of 1912.

1921–40

These were peaceful though not very stable years. It was during this period that photography became an important means for recording and illustrating microscopical material. Black and white film sensitive throughout the visible spectrum (panchromatic) and colour film became available about 1935. Of the ten catalogues for these years in the Science Museum collection, the firms of Baker, Bausch and Lomb, and Leitz produced projection apparatus for tracing a real image. This apparatus was in parallel production with their apparatus for photomicrography. Swift continued to list Wollaston's prism, Ives' cube and Abbe's camera lucida, also an eyepiece camera lucida for use with an inclined microscope. Beck listed a similar drawing eyepiece, Abbe's camera lucida and an Abbe type with

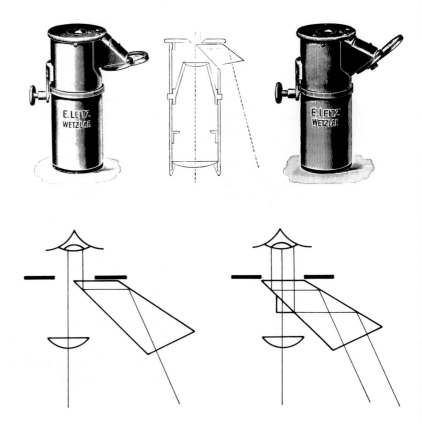

Eyepiece camera lucidas from Leitz catalogue of 1913. Left, for use with a vertical microscope; right, for use with an inclined microscope. The centre diagram shows a split-pupil camera lucida; the diagram in a 1930 catalogue was also a split-pupil type with a small prism on the rhomboid similar to that of Nachet. Both are illustrated in the enlarged drawings below.

an adjustable prism in place of the mirror. The two firms Baker and Watson continued to offer Beale's neutral tint camera lucida. It appears that Watson soon discontinued the large projection prism, their catalogues for 1924, 1926, 1927 and 1928 listing only the camera lucidas of Abbe and Beale, a drawing eyepiece and one drawing table. A Watson 1934 catalogue was without any drawing apparatus; however, a note in

'Watson's Microscope Record' (1939) mentions a Watson–Abbe camera lucida. Leitz and Zeiss produced large and small Abbe camera lucidas and drawing eyepieces. The Leitz drawing eyepiece now had the 'optical hole' of Nachet and the Zeiss eyepiece was also of the split-pupil type camera lucida. Drawing boards were still available from Baker, Swift, Watson and Zeiss. A Zeiss catalogue of 1934 listed a 'Roof Prism on a Slide, for tracing with subjective and projected images in the same position'. A Watson catalogue, 38th edition, not dated but obviously pre-1940, includes a 1946 price list. Some items in the catalogue are not in the price list, but in 1946 it was still possible to buy 'Beale's Neutral-tint Reflector'.

1941–80

This was a period of war followed by considerable economic upheaval. The firms of Beck, Swift and Watson became liquidated or were absorbed by large companies. No doubt there were similar occurrences on the continent, and there are now two Zeiss companies, East and West German. Nevertheless the camera lucida is still produced for use with the microscope, and the beam splitter of the camera lucida has become an integral component for adapting photographic and video cameras to the microscope.

A 1962 leaflet from the Czechoslovakian firm Kovo advertised a camera lucida which had a 'rotating ring with a device for the continuous change of intensity of light which is reflected from the drawing plane'. The size of the ring in the illustration suggests that it rotated a polarising element against a fixed polariser. Neither the drawing nor the text indicates whether the camera lucida is of the Abbe or semi-reflecting cube type. Leitz, in their 1963 catalogue, referred to their drawing apparatus as 'Subjective' and 'Objective'. The former is the camera lucida which included Abbe's

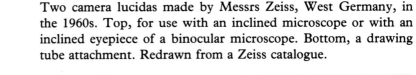

Two camera lucidas made by Messrs Zeiss, West Germany, in the 1960s. Top, for use with an inclined microscope or with an inclined eyepiece of a binocular microscope. Bottom, a drawing tube attachment. Redrawn from a Zeiss catalogue.

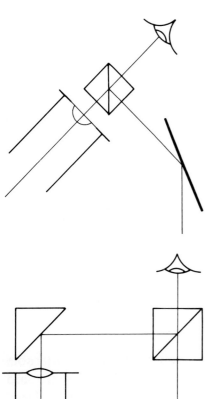

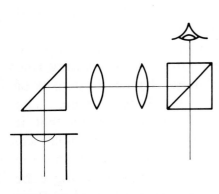

A drawing tube camera lucida by Messrs Zeiss, East Germany. Redrawn from a 1980s catalogue.

large and small instruments and a drawing eyepiece. 'Objective' or real image projection was provided by a small adjustable mirror clamped to the eyepiece tube. The two Zeiss firms now (1982) provide a similar mirror attachment for the eyepiece in order to project a real image; they differ, however, over the camera lucida arrangements. Zeiss, West Germany, supply a semi-reflecting cube prism with a mirror for clamping to the eyepiece tube of an inclined microscope, the drawing being made in front of the microscope. Zeiss, East Germany, also use a cube prism but it is in a tube extending from the side of the microscope at right angles to an inclined eyepiece. The drawing is made on the table at the side of the microscope. The Russian firm Zenit produce a drawing tube which extends horizontally from the body of the microscope between the objective and the eyepiece. At the junction of the microscope and the tube may be placed either a cube prism for camera lucida operation or a normal right-angle prism to project a real image. Leitz also extend a drawing tube from the body of their microscope. It is quite likely that they also employ a cube prism because the literature says 'The microscope image and that of the tracing sheet are superimposed.' A photomicroscope made by Zeiss, West Germany, utilises a thin glass plate and a cube prism as beam splitters for viewing, photography and exposure monitoring. Gillet and Sibert in 1972 produced a video camera incorporating a cube prism for use with a microscope, the prism reflected 20% of the image illumination for viewing and transmitted 80% for the camera.

Of the remaining history of the camera lucida there is little left but the recent literature. However, before turning to the journals, reference should be made to the

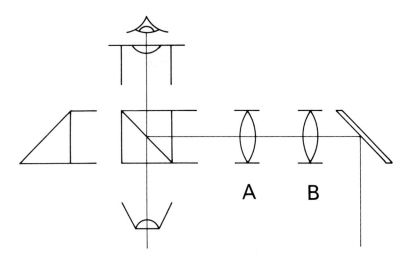

A   B

The Russian firm of Zenith (UK name) made this arrangement for either camera lucida or projection drawing with a microscope. The prisms, in one housing, are brought into operation by turning a milled ring. Lens system A adjusts the magnification of 7 ×, 10 × and 15 ×. Lens system B is to focus the paper and pencil to the image plane of the microscope. Redrawn from a Zenith leaflet, 1980.

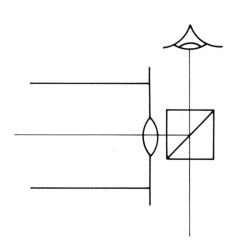

Conrad Beck's semi-silvered prism camera lucida, redrawn from his book *The Microscope* (1921).

confusion of types of camera lucidas made by two respected authors, Conrad Beck and T E Wallis. To the recurring misunderstanding of camera lucida and camera obscura, Beck and Wallis added a muddle of three camera lucidas; the Abbe, Swift–Abbe and Swift–Ives.

Conrad Beck, in his book *The Microscope, a Simple Handbook* (1921), described and illustrated three camera lucidas above the eyepiece and the description says 'The camera lucida is a small half-silvered prism . . . .'[66] One of the three diagrams is referred to as a 'Modified Abbe camera lucida', '. . . in which the bulky mirror is replaced by a small prism attached close to the eyepiece, and the prism is half-silvered.' In fact this is a description of the Swift–Ives camera lucida. Beck repeated the description in the 1930 edition; the 1938 edition said 'The Camera Lucida . . . known as the Abbe Camera Lucida. It consists of a prism with a

161

half-silvered surface... It transmits half the light upwards into the eye...and reflects by means of a large mirror...a beam of light from a paper placed on the table....' This description should have been referred to as a 'Modified Abbe' or a 'Beck–Abbe' camera lucida. Beck continued, 'There is another form of Camera Lucida made for use with the microscope body in a horizontal position, which has a somewhat similar prism and does not require a mirror.' This is vague, it may have been a Beck half-silvered cube prism though it may equally have been a Wollaston prism! It is surprising to find the following from Conrad Beck, 'In another form [of camera lucida] a totally reflecting prism projects an actual image of the object upon the paper....' The projection of an actual image cannot be from any form of camera lucida.

T E Wallis in his book *Analytical Microscopy* (1923) said 'The most convenient type of camera lucida is the Swift–Ives pattern... With this instrument the paper ...is reflected by the small moveable right-angled prism into a second prism above the eye lens of the ocular. The face of this prism is silvered and reflects the light...to the observer's eye, while the microscope image is viewed directly through a small central opening in the silvered surface'.[67] This is a description of the Swift–Abbe camera lucida. Wallis repeated this error in his Presidential Address *Journal of the Royal Microscopical Society* 1955). The 1957 edition of the book illustrates an Abbe camera lucida incorrectly and Wallis said 'Another camera lucida, constructed on the principle of the Abbe instrument is the Swift-Ives pattern in which the plane mirror is replaced by a small right-angled prism.' This and the accompanying drawing is of the Swift–Abbe camera lucida.

Confusion of this nature will, no doubt, continue for some time to come. Beck and Wallis are standard works, and many of the older types of camera lucida are still in use, particularly in the less glamorous laboratories of zoology, botany, medicine and palaeontology.

Ray diagrams of the camera lucidas mentioned by Conrad Beck and T E Wallis. The correct type names should be: A, Abbe; B, Swift–Abbe; C, Swift–Ives; D, described by Beck but not named.

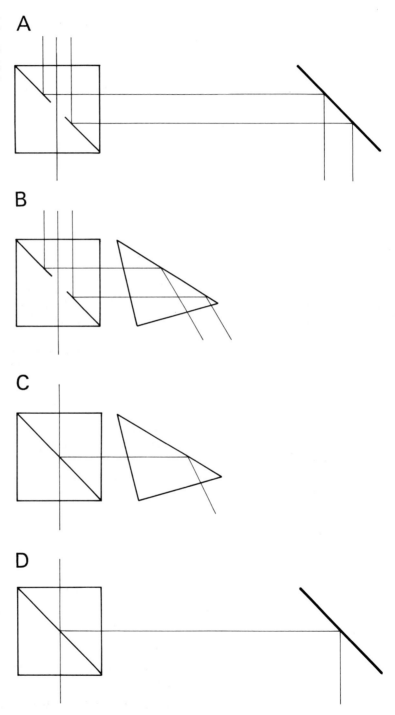

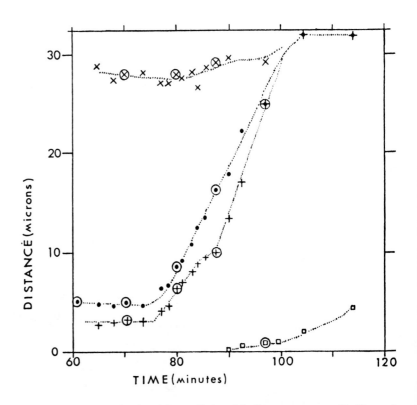

'The data were obtained from living *Nephrotoma suturalis* (Loew) spermatocytes in meiosis-I. The non-circled points were measured from camera-lucida drawings, and the circled points were measured from photographs.' This graph shows the close agreement of measurements made from camera lucida drawings and photographs. The information was obtained from the drawings much more quickly than from the photographs. From Forer A 1968 *Journal of the Royal Microscopical Society.*

There is a tendency among manufacturers to associate the word 'prism' with projection and 'the cube' with camera lucidas. A Zeiss leaflet of 1964 referred, incorrectly, to a cube design as an Abbe camera lucida.

Not surprisingly, there are few journal references of note in the twentieth century. Dr J M Dolby (1958) claimed that it was advantageous to illuminate the drawing paper from underneath.[68] He added that the

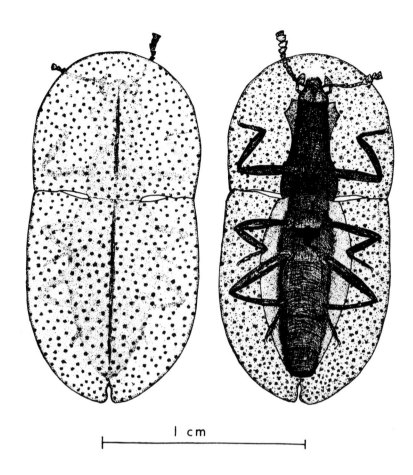

I cm

'Camera lucida drawing of *Cossyphus* sp. from East Africa, showing resemblance to a winged seed. *Left* dorsal, *right* ventral view.' Professor J L Cloudsley-Thompson made these drawings with a Leitz eyepiece camera lucida, occasionally he projected the image onto his drawing. From *The Entomologist's Monthly Magazine* (1978).

pencil marks were more easily seen by transillumination. H A Dade (1963) solved the difficulty of balancing microscope illumination and that of the drawing paper by using crossed polarisers in the light path of the microscope.[69] This method has now become standard commercial practice.

A photomicrograph and a camera lucida drawing showing part of the outline of the minute crustacean *Xestoleberis postangulata*. Dr R H Bate used a large Leitz Abbe camera lucida for the drawing. Scale $D = 200\,\mu m$. (Reproduced by permission of the British Micropalaeontological Society.)

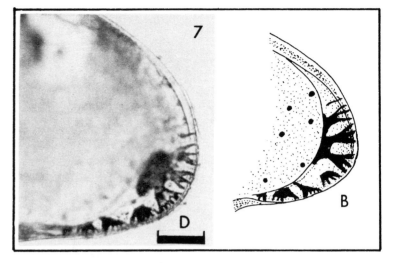

A paper by A Forer (1968) is, perhaps, the most interesting of recent writings on the camera lucida.[70] He described its use for drawing low-contrast objects, and noted the advantage of drawing versus photography. Finally he compared the accuracy of measurements from drawings and photographs. When drawing low-contrast subjects he used matt black paper, a white pencil and red illumination for the drawing area. Forer presented a graph which showed information derived by camera lucida and by photography to be in agreement and, he stated, '. . . the time between observation and having the movement graphs (by camera lucida data) was considerably shorter than with photographic data'.

A photomicrograph and a camera lucida drawing of similar cells from the retina of a cat. The drawing was made by Dr B B Boycott using an Abbe camera lucida. Scale approximately $1\,cm = 1\,\mu m$. (Reproduced by permission of the Royal Society.)

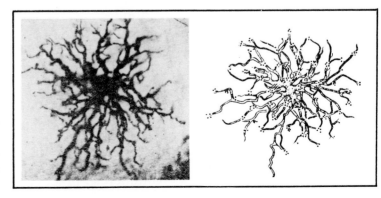

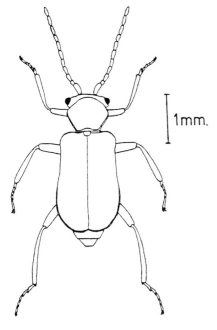

1mm.

Troglops cephalotes (Olivier) female. This drawing was made by R S Key with the aid of a camera lucida. From *The Entomologist's Monthly Magazine* (1983).

Conclusion

We have seen that during the nineteenth century a great variety of camera lucidas was devised for the microscope. Whether they helped or hindered the development of the ideal camera lucida no one can say, but the progress towards that end, though slow, is quite clear. That progress, from glass plates to a semi-reflecting cube prism may be related chronologically as: Wollaston 1806, Amici 1819, *Penny Cyclopaedia* 1839, Govi 1874, Douglas 1880, Aylward 1883 and Ives 1898. More than fifty years were to elapse before the semi-reflecting cube prism was to become the accepted, if not the only, camera lucida for use with the microscope.

References

1. Turner G L'E 1980 *Essays on the History of the Microscope* (Oxford: Senecio)
2. Martin, Benjamin 1771 *Description and Use of a Graphical Perspective and Microscope*
3. Amici, Prof. G B 1819 Le camere lucide *Opuscoli Scientifici* **3** 25–35; 1820 De microscopi catadiottrici *Memorie die Mathematica e di Fisica della Societa Italiana della Scienze* **18** 107–24 Pl. 8
4. Bate R B 1809 Letter *Journal of Natural Philosophy, Chemistry and the Arts* **24** 146–50
5. Hogg, Jabez 1854 *The Microscope* pp. 129–32
6. Quekett J 1848 *Practical Treatise on the Use of the Microscope* pp. 128, 203, 210, 214
7. *Edinburgh Philosophical Journal* 1820 **2** 135–8
8. Lardner D 1855 *Museum of Science and Art* **8** 185–92
9. Carpenter W B *The Microscope and its Revelations* 8 editions 1856–1901

10. *Penny Cyclopaedia* 1839 Microscope p. 188
11. Beale L S *How to Work with the Microscope* 5 editions 1857–80
12. Lankester E 1859 *Half Hours with the Microscope* pp. 23–4
13. Suffolk W T 1870 *On Microscopic Manipulation* pp. 146–55
14. Scourfield D J 1898–1900 Note on Ashe's camera lucida *Journal of the Quekett Microscopical Club* 7 413–15
15. Nelson E M 1895 A new erecting camera lucida *Journal of the Royal Microscopical Society* Ser. 2 **15** 21
16. Douglas J C 1880 The use of silver films in improved instruments of the camera lucida class *Proceedings of the Asiatic Society of Bengal* 73–6 Pl. 1
17. Govi, Prof. G Communication *Atti della Reale Accademia della Scienze di Torrino* **3** 220 (1867–8); **4** 43 (1868–9)
18. Aylward H P 1883 Camera lucida *Journal of the Royal Microscopical Society* Ser. 2 **3** 593
19. Burch G J 1878 On a new micrometer *Journal of the Quekett Microscopical Club* **5** 45–50 Pl. 4
20. Gray P 1860 Improvement of the camera lucida *Quarterly Journal of Microscopical Science* **8** 137 misprinted 713–139
21. Nachet M Jun. 1860 On the camera lucida *Quarterly Journal of Microscopical Science* **8** 156–9
22. *Journal of the Royal Microscopical Society* 1882 Nachet's improved camera lucida Ser. 2 **2** 260
23. *Journal of the Royal Microscopical Society* 1886 Nachet's camera lucida Ser. 2 **6** 1057
24. *Journal of the Royal Microscopical Society* 1886 Malassez's camera lucida Ser. 2 **6** 314
25. *Journal of the Royal Microscopical Society* 1894 Nachet-Govi camera lucida made by Koristka of Milan Ser. 2 **14** 623
26. Maison Nachet 1979 *Catalogues of Stock from 1854–1910* with an introduction by G L'E Turner
27. *Journal of the Royal Microscopical Society* 1882 Abbe's camera lucida Ser. 2 **2** 261–2, 593
28. *Journal of the Royal Microscopical Society* 1883 Abbe's camera lucida Ser. 2 **3** 278–9
29. Anthony J 1884 On drawing prisms *Journal of the Royal Microscopical Society* Ser. 2 **4** 697–703
30. Govi, Prof. G 1874 Sur l'application de la dorure du verre a la construction des chambres claires *Comptes Rendus de l'Academie de Sciences* **79** 373–4
31. Mr Swift 1898 Presidential request *Journal of the Royal Microscopical Society* Ser. 2 **18** 495
32. Swan, Prof. Wm 1861 On the gradual production of luminous impressions on the eye *Transactions of the Royal Society of Edinburgh* **22** 33–9 Pl. 12

33. *Dictionary of Scientific Biography* 1973 Lummer O R (New York: Scribner)
34. *Encyclopaedia Britannica* 1910 Photometry p. 527
35. Walsh, John W T 1958 *Photometry* (London: Constable) p. 4
36. *Encyclopaedic Dictionary of Physics* 1962 (Oxford: Pergamon)
37. Houstoun R A 1915, 1927 *Treatise on Light* (London: Longman) pp. 318–19
38. Clay R S 1911 *Treatise on Practical Light* (London: Macmillan) pp. 392–3
39. Bradbury S 1967 *Evolution of the Microscope* (Oxford: Pergamon) p. 278
40. Swan, Henry 1862 Improvements in stereoscopic apparatus *British Patent* No 3249
41. Russell, Dr J Cunningham 1879 Description of a new form of camera lucida *Journal of the Royal Microscopical Society* **2** 25–6
42. *Journal of the Royal Microscopical Society* 1882 Cramer's camera lucida (also Hofmann's and Oberhauser's) Ser. 2 **2** 679–83
43. Crisp, Frank 1879 On some recent forms of camera lucida *Journal of the Royal Microscopical Society* **2** 21–24 (see note 46)
44. *Journal of the Royal Microscopical Society* 1883 Camerae lucidae of Nobert and of Doyere and Milne-Edwards Ser. 2 **3** 119
45. *Journal of the Royal Microscopical Society* 1883 Chevalier's camera lucida Ser. 2 **3** 423
46. *American Monthly Microscopical Journal* 1882 Grunow's new camera lucida **3** 1; also *Journal of the Royal Microscopical Society* 1883 Ser. 2 **3** 423
47. *Journal of the Royal Microscopical Society* 1883 Seibert and Krafft's small camera lucida Ser. 2 **3** 560
48. Schroeder Dr H 1883 On a new camera lucida *Journal of the Royal Microscopical Society* Ser. 2 **3** 813–15
49. Suffolk W T 1869 On some means of delineating microscopic objects *Journal of the Quekett Microscopical Club* **1** 183–5
50. *Journal of the Royal Microscopical Society* 1883 Drawings and paintings from the microscope Ser. 2 **3** 283–5
51. *Journal of the Quekett Microscopical Club* 1882–4 Conversational meeting Ser. 2 **1** 360
52. *Journal of the Royal Microscopical Society* 1888 Drawings v. photographs (also screen for the Abbe camera lucida) Ser. 2 **3** 809–13
53. *Journal of the Royal Microscopical Society* 1894 Drawing imperfectly visible details with camera lucida Ser. 2 **14** 408

54. *Journal of the Royal Microscopical Society* 1898 Camera drawing Ser. 2 **18** 493

55. *Journal of the Royal Microscopical Society* 1882 Drawing on gelatine with the camera lucida Ser. 2 **2** 262

56. T.R.I. 1879 Hints for the young microscopist. *Hardwicke's Science Gossip* **15** 32

57. *Journal of the Royal Microscopical Society* 1879 Improved mounting for camerae lucidae **2** 954

58. Roberts, Isaac 1872 On a micro-pantograph *Monthly Microscopical Journal* **8** 1–2 Pl XXI

59. *Journal of the Royal Microscopical Society* 1883 Hilgendorf's 'Apparatus for Microscopical Geometrical Drawings' Ser. 2 **3** 279

60. *Library of Useful Knowledge* 1832 Natural philosophy 2 Optical instruments pp. 51–3

61. Hart, Geo W 1866 Microscopic camera-obscura *Hardwicke's Science Gossip* **2** 233

62. Piffard Dr H G 1892 The camera obscura v. the camera lucida *Journal of the Royal Microscopical Society* Ser. 2 **12** 422–3

63. *Journal of the Royal Microscopical Society* 1891 New apparatus for drawing low magnifications Ser. 2 **11** 811

64. Sendall, Sir Walter 1891 On an improved method of making microscopical measurements with the camera lucida *Journal of the Royal Microscopical Society* Ser. 2 **11** 705–9

65. Riddell, Prof 1854 Match photographs, or camera lucida drawings of microscopical objects for the stereoscope, made by means of the ordinary monocular microscope *Quarterly Journal of Microscopical Science* **2** 290–1

66. Beck, Conrad 1921 *The Microscope, a Simple Handbook* pp. 68–72 (Beck)

67. Wallis T E 1923 *Analytical Microscopy* pp. 113–15, 151–163 (London: Arnold)

68. Dolby Dr J M 1958 Note *Journal of the Quekett Microscopical Club* Ser. 4 **5** 108

69. Dade H A 1963 Control of intensity of illumination when using the drawing apparatus *Journal of the Quekett Microscopical Club* **29** 185

70. Forer A 1968 A camera-lucida procedure for low-contrast material. *Journal of the Royal Microscopical Society* **88** 611–13

Part Three

Appendices

The illustration overleaf is one that was frequently used in encyclopaedias and dictionaries in the nineteenth century.

Appendix 1: Misconceptions

In the literature there are many errors of date, and confusion over the exact nature of the camera lucida, and it is more than likely that some authors and teachers have innocently perpetuated these mistakes by accepting 'authoritative' statements. The confusion with Robert Hooke persists, even by such an authority as Edinburgh Museums and Art Galleries in 1984 (see below).

It is possible to read of Wollaston's invention or patent to be in 1804, or 1807, or 1809. A few authors quoted it correctly as 1806 (4 December) but many, particularly in the last century, merely mentioned that it was by Dr Wollaston the chemist or the celebrated Dr Wollaston. The most likely reason for quoting 1807 is that Wollaston published his 'Description' in that year, consequently it was thought the camera lucida was invented and patented in the same year.

An Encyclopaedia of Photography said 'The camera lucida proper was invented by Dr. Wollaston, who died in 1828, but the name was originally given to an instrument invented by Dr. Hooke, analogous to the microscope.'[1] Another curious statement (already noted) came from a dictionary of 1877 which said the camera lucida was 'Founded upon the invention of Baptista Porta (1589), by Dr. Hooke, about 1674. Improved by Wollaston 1805. Phil. Trans. Vol. XXXVIII p. 741.'[2] The *Philosophical Transactions* reference is to Robert Hooke's paper of 1668. Perhaps the oddest statement of all we found in the *Guinness*

Book of Art Facts and Feats which said, 'It was invented by Richard Hooke about 1674.'[3] We have not yet found any special reason for '1674'.

Waterhouse and Gernsheim have already been noted as saying that Robert Hooke referred to a camera lucida, this was repeated in a pamphlet advertising '... the world's first Camera Lucida' at Edinburgh (1984). The pamphlet said 'The term Camera Lucida was first used by Dr. Robert Hooke in a paper delivered to the Royal Society in 1668 ....' This is just not true, Robert Hooke did not use the term. Furthermore he did not use any Latin words in his paper about 'a contrivance'. Many authors[†] seem to have missed the fact that Hooke's paper is about 'a contrivance' not about a 'light room'—a room in which daylight is allowed to enter through uncovered windows, a perfectly normal room. The Edinburgh pamphlet continued 'in which he described a contrivance that would make a picture appear in a fully lit room'. This was followed by a brief description of Hooke's apparatus and, 'Modern television technology has been enlisted to make Hooke's concept a reality ...' This surely is an extraordinary achievement when one remembers that the outdoor cinema has been with us for at least half a century. 'The 20th-century Camera Lucida' is, in fact, a panorama of Edinburgh by closed circuit television; to call it a camera lucida borders on the absurd. However, it does emphasise another confusion, that of the camera lucida with the camera obscura, and, on occasion, with the photographic camera.

The camera lucida is hardly known in the art world where it is thought to be a form of camera obscura or, more usually, that it has something to do with photography. Many scientists, on the other hand, know that it is an instrument in its own right and not merely an accessory for their microscope. Descriptions of the camera lucida sometimes say it produces or throws an image upon the drawing paper; the *English Cyclopaedia*

[†]With the exception of *Encyclopaedia Metropolitana* (1845).

said 'upon a plane or curved surface' which is a direct confusion with the camera obscura.[4] Even recent works have said the camera lucida is a development or an improved version of the camera obscura, being a 'more sophisticated optical instrument incorporating a prism'.[5] It is well known that Sir Francis Chantrey used a camera lucida for preliminary sketches before making a sculpture portrait. A recent book said, 'For this purpose he (Chantrey) used a camera lucida, a forerunner of the modern camera, which projected an image of the object to be drawn onto a plate from which a tracing could be made.'[6] A dictionary of art terms said, 'For practical purposes the portable camera obscura has long been supplanted by the camera lucida and by 20th C. large screen developments.'[7] We find it difficult to believe the author really meant Cinemascope or Cinerama, although the previous sentence said quite rightly that the camera obscura was the forerunner of the modern camera.

To conclude this appendix, reference must be made to the suggested use of a camera lucida by artists who died even before it was invented. In a book on the water-colour artist Thomas Girtin (1775–1802) it was said that, 'Girtin may have used a camera lucida or some similar device...', and later, 'Girtin may have used a camera lucida or some similar optical device....'[8]

Kenneth Clark, in his book *Landscape into Art*, associated the camera lucida with artists of the Golden Age of Dutch art, he wrote, 'In Saenredam the atmosphere is, so to say, used decoratively: in Berckheyde it is uncomfortably reminiscent of the camera lucida; in van der Heyden it reveals a sharpness of detail carried to a point of mania, which the painter manages to communicate to us.'[9] And again, 'By the end of the seventeenth century the painting of light had ceased to be an act of love and had become a trick. The camera lucida was no longer an object of wonder, but an habitual artist's companion.' It is unlikely that Clark was confusing the camera lucida with the camera obscura because he mentioned the latter twice only a dozen pages previously. It was probably a case of knowing the name 'camera lucida' but not the object, though he was aware that such an instrument existed. When writing of the 'light' in Dutch paintings he translated *camera lucida* literally and assumed the Dutch painters had used such an instrument.

A Royal Academy exhibition catalogue referred to the painting of Rosslyn Castle by Paul Sandby (1730–1809).[10] The picture included a lady with a camera obscura on a stand and the catalogue said, 'There is a small study, also in the Mellon collection, of the woman drawing with the aid of a camera lucida.' Whilst it is true that Sandby died a short while after the invention of the camera lucida the painting is thought to have been made about 1770.

References

Dates for the invention or patent of the camera lucida.
1804   Marion (1868) Ganot (1890, 1898)
1807   *Dictionary of Arts, Sciences and Manufactures* (1842)
        Dubery and Willats (1972)
        Edinburgh Encyclopaedia (1830)
        Encyclopaedia Britannica (1973)
        Haydn's Book of Dates (1889)
        London Encyclopaedia (1829)
        Manual of Dates (1877)
1809   Gehler (1826)
        Marbach (1850)

1. *Encyclopaedia of Photography* 1879 (reprint 1947) (New York: Arno) p. 74
2. Knight E H 1877 *Practical Dictionary of Mechanics* p. 434
3. Mills J F M 1978 *Guinness Book of Art Facts and Feats* (London: Guinness Superlatives)
4. *English Cyclopaedia* 1891 pp. 532–3
5. Murray P and Murray L 1968 *Dictionary of Art and Artists* p. 67

6. Potts A 1981 *Sir Francis Chantrey 1781–1841* (London: National Portrait Gallery) p. 8

7. Mayer R 1969 *Dictionary of Art Terms and Techniques* (London: A and C Black) p. 58

8. Girtin T and Loshak D 1954 *The Art of Thomas Girtin* (London: A and C Black) pp. 35, 39

9. Clark, Kenneth 1976 *Landscape into Art* (London: Murray) p. 65

10. Royal Academy Catalogue 1972 *English Drawings and Water-Colours 1550–1850 in the Collection of Mr & Mrs Paul Mellon* (London: Royal Academy of Arts) p. 28

Appendix 2: Camera Lucidas in Three Museum Collections

Camera lucidas at the Science Museum, South Kensington, Optics (Opt) and Chemistry (Ch) Departments (March 1985)

Maker	Type	Inventory Number
Anon	Mirror and lens	1928–937 Opt
	Prism and glass plate	1928–907 Opt
	Wollaston, 3193 on prism, 'Colonel Codrington' on case	1980–1831 Ch
	Wollaston 244 on prism	1980–1832 Ch
	895 on prism†	1912–207 Opt
	3313 or 3373 on prism	1981–268/10 Opt
	801 on prism 504 on mount	1981–268/11 Opt
	802 on prism 505 on mount	1981–268/8 Opt
	621 on prism	1981–268/9 Opt
	prism missing	1981–268/12 Opt
	eleven instruments	1981–268/3, 7, 13, 15, 16, 18, 19, 21, 22, Opt
		1981–107 Opt
		1983–186 Opt
Adie	Wollaston	1981–268/4 Opt
Alexander	Mirror and Glass plate no 1397	1912–206 Opt
Bancks	Wollaston	1983–284 Opt
Berville (Lechertier Barbe)	Right-angle prism	1980–1924 Opt
Boucart	Wollaston	1977–527 Ch
Cary	Wollaston	1977–526 Ch
		1981–268/6, /17 Opt
	Prism and glass plate	1934–152 Opt

† Scratched *ccee* on the other face of the right angle

178

Camera lucidas at the Science Museum, S. Kensington 2

Maker	Type	Inventory Number
Diament	Single reflector	1987–277 Opt
Dollond	Wollaston	1981–268/20 Opt
Ebsworth		1906–81 Opt
Ladd		1872–16 Opt
Lutz		1876–326 Opt
(Laussedat)		
Nachet	Govi cube on a low-power microscope	1920–776 Opt
Phantom Line Graphics	Single reflector	1983–1199 Opt
Pillischer	Wollaston	1981–268/1, /5 Opt
Swift	Govi cube microscope attachment no 31057	1980–761 Opt
Varley	Graphic Telescope no 37	1921–814 Opt
	Graphic Telescope	1921–818 Opt
	Graphic Telescope	1907–102 Opt
	Graphic Telescope	1981–75 Opt
Watkins & Hill	Wollaston	1981–268/2 Opt
Watson	Govi cube microscope attachment	1980–762 Opt
	Right-angle prism microscope attachment no 282. This may be for projection.	1921–880 Opt
West	Wollaston	1981–268/14 Opt
Zeiss	Abbe microscope attachment	1983–1054 Opt
		1889–40 Opt
	Two prisms, microscope attachment	1982–1552 Opt

Number of camera lucidas of each type

33	Wollaston's prism
1	Other split-pupil type
4	See-through type—mirror or prism and glass plate
2	Single-reflector
4	Graphic Telescope
7	Microscope attachments

Camera Lucidas at the Whipple Museum of the History of Science, Cambridge (May 1985)

Maker	Type	Inventory Number
Anon	Wollaston in a mount with a diaphragm plate only	583
	Wollaston 1882 on prism	93
	Wollaston	1549
	Wollaston, incomplete with a number of unfinished parts	3094
	Wollaston, front face convex focal length about 50 mm, in wood mount, no stand. Described by Gunther as Wollaston's prototype	1106
Alexander	Mirror and glass plate	498
Troughton and Simms	Wollaston	2829
Varley	Graphic Telescope	69
Watkins and Hill	Wollaston	1265

Camera Lucidas at the Royal Scottish Museum, Edinburgh

Maker	Type	Inventory Number
Anon	Soemmering	1979.59
	Wollaston	1973.95
		1975.1
		1979.60
Adie	Amici–Chevalier	1933.65
	Wollaston	1975.2
Amici	Amici–Chevalier	1936.114
		1979.46
Beck	Wollaston	1950.21
		1984.6

Appendix 2

Camera Lucidas at the Royal Scottish Museum, Edinburgh

Maker	Type	Inventory Number
Berville	Right-angle prism	1983.209
Bryson	Wollaston	1980.237
King	Wollaston	1875.27.1
Smith	Wollaston	1980.2
Smith and Beck	Wollaston	1979.28
		1979.65
Swift	Wollaston	1983.214

Appendix 3:
British Patents

Year	Number	Name and Title
1806	2993	Wollaston, William Hyde. An instrument whereby any Person may draw in perspective, or may copy or reduce any print or drawing
1811	3430	Varley, Cornelius. A new construction of a telescope or optical instrument for viewing distant objects, and for other useful purposes, with a suitable table or stand for the same
1836	7052	Parlour, Samuel. Certain improvements applicable to sketching, drawing or delineating, which I intend to denominate Parlour's Sketching Case
1873	2232	Varley, Frederick Henry. Improvements in transmitting and recording telegraph signals, and means of transcribing, and apparatus connected therewith
1892	17 837	Bonne, Christen Rees, acting for Eppers, Heinrich of Brunswick. An improved apparatus for executing drawings by means of a 'Camera Lucida'
1895	15 113	Harris, Arthur. Improvements in apparatus for copying drawings and the like
1899	11 556	Schmidt, Hans. Improvement in prisms for optical purposes
1900	22 891	Buchberger, Georg, of Landshut, Lower Bavaria. Improvements in apparatus for producing drawings in perspective from geometrical sketches and the like

Year	Number	Name and Title
1902	787	Bruyn, J de. Improvements in apparatus for comparing handwriting or other objects
1934	416 646	Marx and Co. Drawing apparatus for reproducing pictures, designs and the like
1934	430 508	Sothern, J M S. Improvements in or relating to optical copying apparatus
1934	443 744	Microphone Corporation of America. Optical reproducing device
1938	534 915	Seely, H E. Map making and apparatus therefor
1952	749 306	Compagnie pour la Fabrication des Compteurs et Material d'Usines a Gaz. Improvements in or relating to anti-parallax devices
1953	749 463	Margary, A R. Device for demonstrating the appearance of fabrics
1953	755 451	Radio Corporation of America. Information plotting apparatus
1958	890 791	English Electric Co. Ltd. Improvements in and relating to navigational aids
1960	906 110	Standard Telephones and Cables Ltd. Improvements in or relating to optical combining arrangements

Bibliography

The authors' collection of notes, references and material on the camera lucida is now at the Science Museum Library, South Kensington, London.

Abbe, Prof E 1882, 1883, 1884, 1894, 1899 Notes on Abbe's camera lucida *Journal of the Royal Microscopical Society* Ser. 2 **2 3 4 14 19**

—— 1895 Abbe–Czapski camera lucida *Journal of the Quekett Microscopical Club* Ser. 2 **5**

Abbott A S 1973 *Ordinary Level Physics* (London: Heineman)

Abbott W 1950 *Theory and Practice of Perspective* (Glasgow: Blackie)

Alexander, Alexander nd *c.* 1830 *The Graphic Mirror*

Allison A C and Chacko L 1949 The use of a camera lucida for micrometry and counts of nerve fibres and other small objects *Journal of the Royal Microscopical Society* **69**

Altick R D 1978 *The Shows of London* (Cambridge, MA: Harvard University Press)

Amici, Prof. G B 1819 Le camere lucide *Opuscoli Scientifici* **3**

—— 1820 De' microscopi catadiottrici *Memorie di Mathematica e di Fisica della Societa Italiana della Scienze*

—— 1820 Account of an improved catadioptrical microscope by Prof. Amici *Edinburgh Philosophical Journal* **2**

—— 1823 Sur la chambre claire *Annales de Chimie et de Physique* **22**

Andrews G F 1898 Camera drawing *Journal of the Royal Microscopical Society* Ser. 2 **18**

Anthony, Dr J 1884 *Journal of the Royal Microscopical Society* Ser. 2 **4**

Arnott, Neil 1829 *Elements of Physics or Natural Philosophy*

Ashe, A see Scourfield D J

Aubrey, John 1978 *Brief Lives* ed O L Dick (Harmondsworth: Penguin)

Aylward H P 1883 Camera lucida *Journal of the Royal Microscopical Society* Ser. 2 **3**

B, J O 1830 *Mechanics' Magazine* **3**

Baddely Wm Jun 1830 *Mechanics' Magazine* **3**

184

Bibliography

Barron A L E 1965 *Using the Microscope* (London: Chapman and Hall)

Bartlett W H 1844 *Walks about the City and Environs of Jerusalem*

Bate R B 1809 On the camera lucida *Journal of Natural Philosophy, Chemistry and the Arts* **24**

Bate R H and Sheppard L M 1980 On *Xestoleberis postangulata*, Bate and Sheppard sp. nov. *A Stereo-Atlas of Ostracod Shells*

Bauerfeind, Herr 1868 Ueber eine neue Eigenschaft des Prismas der Camera Lucida *Akademie der Wissenschaften zu Munchen*

Bausch and Lomb Optical Co. 1883 Fitting for neutral tint camera lucida *Journal of the Royal Microscopical Society* Ser. 2 **3**

—— 1905 Improved form of camera lucida *Journal of the Royal Microscopical Society* **25**

Beale, Dr L S 1857, 1861, 1864, 1868, 1880 *How to work with the Microscope* (London: Churchill (1, 2 edn), Harrison (3, 4, 5 edn))

Beck, Conrad 1921, 1930, 1938 *The Microscope, A Simple Handbook* (Beck)

Bell, Michael and Cooke, W Martha 1978 The last 'Lion'—*Rambles in Quebec with James Pattison Cockburn* exhibition catalogue, Agnes Etherington Art Centre, Ontario, Canada

Biot J B 1821 *Precis Elementaire de Physique Experimentale*

Bolton A T 1939 Cotman and Charles Barry in Rouen *Journal of the Royal Institute of British Architects* (June)

Boycott B B *et al* 1978 Morphological types of horizontal cell in the retina of the domestic cat *Proc. R. Soc. B* **203** 229–45

Bradbury S 1967 *Evolution of the Microscope* (Oxford: Pergamon)

Brewster D 1813 *Treatise on New Philosophical Instruments*

—— 1831 *Treatise on Optics*

—— 1856 *The Stereoscope*

Brewster D and Harris Wm 1811 *British Patent* No 3453

Brocher F 1910 Drawing with a camera lucida *Journal of the Royal Microscopical Society* **30**

Burch G J 1878–9 On a new micrometer *Journal of the Quekett Microscopical Club* **5**

Cambridge Philosophical Society 1936 Exhibition of Historic Scientific Apparatus in Cambridge *Catalogue*

Carpenter W B 1856, 1857, 1862, 1868, 1875, 1881, 1891, 1900 *The Microscope and its Revelations* (London: Churchill)

'Caret' 1853 Camera lucida *Notes and Queries* **8**

Caspar M and Hammer F 1941 *Johannes Kepler Gesammelte Werke* vol. 4 (Munich)

Chevalier, Charles 1833 *Notice sur l'usage des Chambres Obscures et Chambres Claires*

Journal of the Royal Microscopical Society 1883 Chevalier's Camera Lucida Ser. 2 **3**

185

Bibliography

Chevallier J G A 1815 *Le Conservateur de la Vue*
Chladni, Dr 1819 Einige wissenchaftliche Nachrichien aus Munchen...und einer neuen Art Camera Lucida *Annalen der Physik*
Citert P H Van 1934 *Descriptive catalogue of the Microscopes at Utrecht University Museum*
Clark, Kenneth 1976 *Landscape into Art* (London: Murray)
Clay R S 1911 *Treatise on Practical Light* (London: Macmillan)
Cloudsley-Thompson J L 1978 The genus *Cossyphus* (Col. Tenebrionidae) *Entomologist's Monthly Magazine*
Cobb N A 1906 Construction and fittings of a microscope room *Journal of the Royal Microscopical Society* **26**
Coddington H 1823, 1825 *Elementary Treatise on Optics*
—— 1830 *Treatise on the Eye and Optical Instruments*
Coles H 1854 On the use of the camera lucida as a micrometer *Quarterly Journal of Microscopical Science* **2**
The Connoisseur 1943 Cornelius Varley
Constable W G 1954 *Painter's Workshop* (Oxford: Oxford University Press)
Coon J M 1939 Camera lucida drawing *Watson's Microscope Record* **46**
Cramer, Dr C 1882 Notes on camera lucidas of Hofmann, Oberhauser and a home-made model *Journal of the Royal Microscopical Society* Ser. 2 **2**
Creteur M 1882 Drawing on gelatine with the camera lucida *Journal of the Royal Microscopical Society* Ser. 2 **2**
Crisp F 1879 On some recent forms of camera lucida *Journal of the Royal Microscopical Society* **2**
Cumberland, George Jr nd ?1815 *Views in Spain and Portugal taken during the Campaigns of His Grace the Duke of Wellington, By George Cumberland, Jr., only 30 Copies Printed*
Curtice, Dr C 1891 A method of drawing microscopic objects by the use of co-ordinates *Journal of the Royal Microscopical Society* Ser. 2 **11**
Journal of the Royal Microscopical Society 1882 Curtis's camera lucida drawing arrangement Ser. 2 **2**
D, E T 1884 Note on drawing with a camera lucida *Journal of the Royal Microscopical Society* Ser. 2 **4**
Dade H A 1963 Control of intensity of illumination when using the drawing apparatus *Journal of the Quekett Microscopical Club* **29**
Dawes B 1942 Use of the camera lucida for transcribing diagrams *Nature* **149**
Deflandre G 1947 Microscopie pratique (Paris: Lechevalier)

Bibliography

Dictionaries and Encyclopaedias
   American Cyclopaedia 1860
   Barlow P 1814 *A New Mathematical and Philosophical Dictionary*
   British Cyclopaedia 1809, 1835
   Bryan M 1895 *Dictionary of Painters and Engravers*
   Century Dictionary 1889
   Chambers's Encyclopaedia 1874, 1950
   Cyclopaedia 1819
   Dictionary of Art and Artists 1965
   Dictionary of Art Terms and Techniques 1969
   Dictionary of the Arts, Sciences and Manufactures 1842
   Dictionary of Mechanical Science, Arts, Manufactures, etc 1827
   Dictionary of National Biography 1899, 1900, 1908, (2nd
      Supplement 1912, reprinted 1920) (Oxford: Oxford University
      Press)
   Dictionary of Scientific Biography 1970, 1973
   Dictionnaire General des Sciences Theoriques et Appliques 1864
   *Dictionnaire Technologique ou Nouveau Dictionnaire Universel
      des Arts et Metiers* 1823
   Edinburgh Encyclopaedia 1830
   Encyclopaedia of the Arts 1966
   Encyclopaedia Britannica 1823, Suppl. 1824, 1875–89, 1910,
      1957, 1973
   Encyclopaedia Londinensis 1810
   Encyclopaedia Metropolitana 1845
   Encyclopaedia of Photography 1879 (reprint 1947) (New York:
      Arno)
   Encyclopaedic Dictionary of Physics 1962
   English Cyclopaedia 1891
   Gehler J S T 1826 *Physikalisches Wortbuch*
   Good J M *et al* 1813 *Pantologia*
   Griffith J W and Henfrey A 1856 *Micrographic Dictionary*
   Harmsworth Encyclopaedia 1906, nd *c.* 1920
   Haydn's Dictionary of Dates 1889
   Hutton, Chas 1795, 1815 *A Mathematical and Philosophical
      Dictionary*
   Imperial Dictionary of the English Language 1898
   Knight E H 1877 *Practical Dictionary of Mechanics*
   London Encyclopaedia 1829
   Marbach O 1850 *Physikalisches Lexikon*
   McGraw Hill Encyclopaedia of Science and Technology 1982
   Micrographic Dictionary 1856
   Nouvelle Biographie Generale 1963
   Oxford Companion to Art 1970

Pantologia 1813

Penny Cyclopaedia 1836, 1839

Disney A N (ed) 1928 *Origin and Development of the Microscope—Instruments at the Royal Microscopical Society* (London: Royal Microscopical Society)

Distortion 1893 *Journal of the Quekett Microscopical Club* Ser. 2 **5**

Dolby, Dr J M 1958 Pupitre a dessiner lumineux facilitant l'emploi de l'appareil a mirroir dans le dessin au microscope *Annales de Parasitologie Humaine et Comparee* **33**

—— 1958 *Journal of the Quekett Microscopical Club* Ser. 4 **5**

Dollond G nd ?1830 *Description of the Camera Lucida . . . to which is added . . . a letter . . . by Capt. Basil Hall*

Douglas J C 1880 The use of silver films in improved instruments of the camera lucida class *Proceedings of the Asiatic Society of Bengal*

Doyere and Milne-Edwards 1883 Camerae lucidae of Nobert and of Doyere and Milne-Edwards *Journal of the Royal Microscopical Society* Ser. 2 **3**

Draper E T 1883 Drawings and paintings from the microscope *Journal of the Royal Microscopical Society* Ser. 2 **3**

Dubery F and Willats J 1972, 1983 *Drawing Systems* (Herbert)

Dumaige M 1888 Camera lucida *Journal of the Royal Microscopical Society* Ser. 2 **8**

E, J 1830 Camera lucida *Mechanics' Magazine* **3**

Edinburgh Journal of Science 1825 Professor Amici's improved camera lucidas **3**

Edinburgh New Philosophical Journal 1841

Edinger, Dr L 1891 New apparatus for drawing low magnifications *Journal of the Royal Microscopical Society* Ser. 2 **11**

Edmund Scientific Co. nd *c.* 1980 *'Lucy' makes you an Artist.* Fun with Optics

—— nd *c.* 1982 *Optical Drawing Devices* Popular Optics Library

Eternod, Prof. A 1888 Drawing board *Journal of the Royal Microscopical Society* Ser. 2 **8**

Evans D S *et al* (eds) 1969 *Herschel at the Cape* (Texas)

Feldhaus F M 1914 *Die Technik*

Ferris C F 1928 *Principles of Systematic Entomology* (Stanford)

Fletcher D S A revision of the Old World genus *Zamarada* (Lepidoptera: Geometridae) *Bulletin of the British Museum (Natural History) Entomology*

Forer A 1968 A Camera-lucida procedure for low-contrast material *Journal of the Royal Microscopical Society* **88**

Francotte M P 1883 Description d'une Chambre-claire *Bulletin des Seances, Societe Belge de Microscopie* **10**

—— 1883 *Journal of the Royal Microscopical Society* Ser. 2 **3**

Ganot A 1890 *Elementary Treatise of Physics* (transl. E Atkinson)

Gell, Sir Wm 1832 *Pompeiana*

Gentleman's Magazine 1829 Dr. Wollaston, F.R.S. Obituary. Supplement to **99**

Gernsheim H 1955 *History of Photography* (London: Oxford University Press)

Girtin T and Loshak D 1954 *The Art of Thomas Girtin* (London: Black)

Goethart, Dr J W Chr 1894 Drawing imperfectly visible details with a camera lucida *Journal of the Royal Microscopical Society* Ser. 2 **14**

Goring C R and Pritchard A 1830 *Microscopic Illustrations of Living Objects*

—— 1837 *Micrographia*

Govi, Prof. G 1867–8, 1868–9 Communications *Atti della Reale Accademia della Scienze di Torino* **3**, **4**

—— 1872–73 Di alcune nuove Camere-lucide *Atti della Reale Accademia della Scienze di Torino* **8**

—— 1874 Sur l'application de la dorure du verre a la construction des chambres claires *Comptes Rendus de l'Academie de Sciences* **79**

—— 1875 Gilded glass in the construction of the camera lucida *Monthly Microscopical Journal* **13**

—— 1889 Intorno una nuova camera-lucida *Atti della R. Accademia die Lincei* **5**

'Graphoscope' *c.* 1960 (E and S, England)

Gray P 1860 Improvement of the camera lucida *Quarterly Journal of Microscopical Science* **8**

Great Exhibition 1851 *Official Descriptive and Illustrated Catalogue* 3 vols

Grehn, Prof. J 1977 *Leitz Microscopes for 125 Years* (Leitz)

Griffith J W and Henfrey A 1856 *Micrographic Dictionary*

Grunow J 1882 New camera lucida *American Monthly Microscopical Journal* **3** November

Grunow's camera lucida 1883 *Journal of the Royal Microscopical Society* Ser. 2 **3**

Guinness Book of Art Facts and Feats 1978

Gunther R T 1937 *Early Science in Cambridge* (Oxford: Oxford University Press)

H, K 1841 New optical drawing instrument *Mechanics' Magazine*

Hagen, Victor Wolfgang von 1950 *F Catherwood* (Barre, MA: Barre)

Hall, Capt. Basil, RN 1829 *Forty Etchings from Sketches made with the Camera Lucida in North America in 1827 and 1829*

Bibliography

—— 1829 *Travels in North America*

—— 1839 Drawing and description of the capstan lately recovered from the *Royal George. United Service Journal* (November) (also a separate publication at the British Library); see also Dollond G

Hammond, John H 1981 *The Camera Obscura* (Bristol: Adam Hilger)

Hardie, Martin 1967 *Water-colour Painting in Britain* (London: Batsford)

Harding J P 1941 Simple modifications of the camera lucida for making larger drawings *Nature* **148**

Hardy J D 1882–4 On drawing *Journal of the Quekett Microscopical Club* Ser. 2 **1**

—— 1896 Distortion discussion *Journal of the Quekett Microscopical Club* Ser. 2 **6**

Hart G W 1866 Microscopic camera-obscura *Science Gossip* **2**

Harvey C 1960 An easily made drawing apparatus *Journal of the Quekett Microscopical Club* Ser. 4 **5**

Hasted H 1849 Reminiscences of Dr. Wollaston *Proceedings of the Bury and W. Suffolk Archaeological Institute* **1**

Helmholtz H von 1909–11 *Handbuch de Physiologischen Optik* (Engl. transl. 1924 Southall J P C *Physiological Optics*)

Hilgendorf, Dr F 1883 Apparatus for microscopical geometrical drawing *Journal of the Royal Microscopical Society* Ser. 2 **3**

Hogg, Jabez 1854 *The Microscope*

—— 1861 *Elements of Experimental and Natural Philosophy*

Holle's drawing apparatus 1883 *Journal of the Royal Microscopical Society* Ser. 2 **3**

Hooke, Robert 1667 *Micrographia*

—— 1668 A Contrivance to make the picture of any thing appear on a wall . . . etc *Philosophical Transactions of the Royal Society* No 38

Horner W G 1815 New and important combinations with the camera lucida *Annals of Philosophy* **6**

Hornor, Thomas 1813 *A Description of an Improved Method of Delineating Estates*

—— c 1819 *Album of Water-colour Paintings of the Vale of Neath* (British Museum Print Room)

—— 1823 *Prospectus: View of London*; see also page . . . .

Hoskins G A 1837 *Visit to the Great Oasis of the Libyan Desert*

Houstoun R A 1915, 1927 *A Treatise on Light*

Hyde, Ralph 1977 Thomas Hornor: pictural land surveyor *Imago Mundi* **29**

—— 1982 *The Regent's Park Colosseum* (London: Ackermann)

I, T R 1879 Hints for the young microscopist *Science Gossip* **15**

Illustrated London News 1873 Obituary, Cornelius Varley **63**

Imboden W 1909 A simple drawing and projection apparatus for microscopical low power objects *Journal of the Quekett Club* Ser. 2 **10**

Ives F H 1898 Camera lucida *Journal of the Royal Microscopical Society* Ser. 2 **18**

J 1829 Utility of the camera lucida *Mechanics' Magazine* **2**

J, H 1830 Description of the camera lucida with specimens of drawings *Mechanics' Magazine* **3**

Jenkins, Elis 1971 Thomas Hornor *Stewart William's Glamorgan Historian* **7** (Cowbridge: Brown)

Johnston T B 1853 Camera lucida *Notes and Queries* **8**

Jones, George 1849 *Sir Francis Chantrey, R.A. Recollections of his Life, Practice and Opinions*

Jones, H Festing 1919 *Samuel Butler, author of Erewhon (1803–1902) a Memoir*

Jones, Thomas 1807 Description of the optigraph *Philosophical Magazine* **27**

Jung's new drawing apparatus (Embryograph) 1884 *Journal of the Royal Microscopical Society* Ser. 2 **4**

'Juvenile Reader' 1830 Camera lucida *Mechanics' Magazine* **3**

Kauffmann C M 1984 *John Varley, 1778–1842* (Batsford/Victoria and Albert Museum)

Kay, H Isherwood 1925–6 *John Sell Cotman's Letters from Normandy* (Walpole Society/Oxford University Press)

Kepler J 1611 *Dioptrice*; see also Caspar M and Hammer F

Key R S 1983 *Troglops cephalotes* (Olivier) (Col. Melyridae) *Entomologist's Monthly Magazine* **119**

Keysor,— 1829 The pentagraph *Mechanics' Magazine* **2**

King H C 1954 Life and optical work of W. H. Wollaston *British Journal of Physiological Optics* **11**

Kitson S D 1932-3 *Notes on a Collection of Portrait Drawings formed by Dawson Turner* (Walpole Society/Oxford University Press)

—— 1937 *John Sell Cotman* (London: Faber)

Kitton F 1879 New forms of camera lucida (Hofmann) *Science Gossip* **15**

Kohl G 1884 Note on Abbe's camera lucida *Journal of the Royal Microscopical Society* Ser. 2 **4**

Koristka 1894 Nachet/Govi camera lucida *Journal of the Royal Microscopical Society* Ser. 2 **14**

Koristka's Abbe camera lucida with lens holder 1903 *Journal of the Royal Microscopical Society* **23**

Kruines M 1838 Optique: chambre claire *Comptes Rendus des Seances de l'Academie des Sciences* **5**; also 1838 *Loudon's Architectural Magazine*

Lafay A 1900 Sur deux applications de la chambre claire de Govi *Comptes Rendus des Seances de l'Academie des Sciences* **130**

Langeron M 1949 *Precis de Microscopie* (Masson)

Lankester E 1859 *Half Hours with the Microscope*

Lardner D 1855 *Museum of Science and Art* **8**

Ledermuller M F 1760 *Microscopischer Gemuths und Augenergotzung* (Nurnburg)

Leitz camera lucida 1893 *Journal of the Quekett Microscopical Club* **5**

Leitz, Messrs 1913, 1930 *Catalogues*

Leyser, Baron Ernest von 1842 Erlauternde Worte zu der Camera Clara Dioptrice *Annalen der Physik und Chemie* **56**

Library of Useful Knowledge Natural Philosophy **2** 1832 Optical instruments

London Mechanics' Register 1826 Dr. Wollaston's camera lucida **2**

Loshak D see Girtin T

Loudon's Architectural Magazine 1838 New camera lucida—M Kruines

Ludicke A F 1812 Beschreibung einer veranderten Camera Lucida *Annalen der Physik* **36**

Magazine of Science 1840 Varley's graphic microscope and telescope, Wollaston's camera lucida, Amici's camera lucida and Alexander's Graphic Mirror **2**

—— 1841 A simple camera lucida *ibid.* **3**

Malassez, Prof. L 1879 Improved mounting for camerae lucidae *Journal of the Royal Microscopical Society* **2**

—— 1883 Correction of the distortion produced by the camera lucida *ibid.* Ser. 2 **3**

Malassez's camera lucida 1886 *Journal of the Royal Microscopical Society* Ser. 2 **6**

Marion F 1868 *Wonders of Optics* (Engl. transl. C W Quin)

Martin, Benjamin 1771 *Description and use of a Graphical Perspective and Microscope*

Mechanics' Magazine 1829, 1830

Micrographic Dictionary 1856

Mills J F M 1978 *Guinness Book of Art Facts and Feats*

Myerscough-Walker R 1958 *The Perspectivist*

Minod M 1928 A new stand for drawing in a camera clara *Nature* **122**

Nachet A 1929 *Collection Nachet* (Paris)

Nachet M Jun 1860 On the camera lucida *Quarterly Journal of Microscopical Science* **8**

—— 1882 Nachet's improved camera lucida *Journal of the Royal Microscopical Society* Ser. 2 **2**

—— 1886 Nachet's camera lucida *ibid.* Ser. 2 **6**

Bibliography

—— 1882 Nouvelle chambre claire *Seances de la Societe Française de Physique*

Nachet, Maison 1979 *Catalogues of Stock from 1854–1910* introduction by G L'E Turner (Paris: Brieux)

Nedoluha A 1959 Kultergeschichte des technischen Zeichens *Blatter fur Technikgeschiechte* **21**

Nelson E M 1894 On a new camera lucida *Journal of the Quekett Microscopical Club* Ser. 2 **6**

—— 1894 Correction of Beale's camera lucida *ibid.*

—— 1895 A new erecting camera lucida *Journal of the Royal Microscopical Society* Ser. 2 **15**

—— 1896 Distortion *Journal of the Quekett Microscopical Club* Ser. 2 **6**

Newnes Practical Mechanics 1955 Camera obscura . . . details of the camera lucida

Nobert 1883 Camerae lucidae of Nobert and of Doyere and Milne-Edwards *Journal of the Royal Microscopical Society* Ser. 2 **3**

Nollet, M l'Abbe 1756 *Leçons de Physique Experimentale*

Nuovo Cimento 1868

Nuttall R H 1977 Andrew Pritchard, optician and microscope maker *The Microscope* **25**

Oldroyd H 1958 *Collecting, Preserving and Studying Insects* (London: Hutchinson)

Palmer F D 1892 *Leaves from the Diary and Journal of the late Charles J. Palmer, F.S.A.*

Paris J A 1831 *Life of Sir Humphrey Davy* 2 vol. edn

Parlour S 1836 *British Patent* No 7052

Payne B O 1957 *Microscope Design and Construction* (Cooke, Troughton and Simms)

Pellerin M 1878 Optique, sur une chambre claire *Comptes Rendus de l'Academie des Sciences* **83**

Penny Cyclopaedia 1839 The microscope

Peterson, Alvah 1964 *Entomological Techniques* (Michigan: Edwards)

Phillips T *Letter to Dawson Turner* (Trinity College Library, Cambridge)

Pidgley, Michael 1972 Cornelius Varley, Cotman and the Graphic Telescope *Burlington Magazine*

Pierpont F H 1896 *British Patent* No 23 397

Piersol, Dr G A 1888 Drawings v. photographs (also a screen for the Abbe camera lucida) *Journal of the Royal Microscopical Society* Ser. 2 **8**

Piffard, Dr H G 1892 The camera obscura v. the camera lucida *Journal of the Royal Microscopical Society* Ser. 2 **12**

193

Bibliography

Potts A 1981 *Sir Francis Chantrey, 1781–1841, Sculptor of the Great* (London: National Portrait Gallery)

Pritchard, Andrew 1827 On the Art of forming diamonds into single lenses for microscopes *Quarterly Journal of Science, Literature and Art* (July-December)

—— 1832 *The Microscope Cabinet*

Quekett, John 1848 *Practical Treatise on the use of the Microscope*

Quin C W (transl.) see Marion F

Rajnai, Miklos and Allthorpe-Guyton, Marjorie 1975 *Drawings of Normandy in Norwich Castle Museum* (Norwich)

Rees' Cyclopaedia 1820

Reichert, — 1899 Camera lucida *Journal of the Royal Microscopical Society* Ser. 2 **19**

Reichert, Messrs 1909 *Catalogue*

Riddell, Prof. 1854 Match photographs, or camera lucida drawings of microscopical objects for the stereoscope *Quarterly Journal of Microscopical Science* **2**

Roberts, Isaac 1827 On a micro-pantograph *Monthly Microscopical Journal* **8**

Robison, Sir John 1841 A simple camera lucida *Magazine of Science* **3**

—— 1841 letter *Edinburgh New Philosophical Journal* **30**

Roget J L 1891 *History of the Old Water Colour Society* (London: Longman)

Romer, John 1981 *Valley of the Kings* (London: Michael Joseph/ Rainbird)

Ronchi, Vasco 1963 Giovan Battista Amici, optician (in English) *Publicazioni dell'Istituto Nazionale di Ottica* Ser. II No. 1035 (translated from *La Ricerca Scientifica* Anno 33 Ser. 2 **3**)

Ross, Messrs 1875 *Catalogue*

Roundell, James 1974 *Thomas Shotter Boys* (Octopus)

Rousselet M 1894 Home made camera lucida *Journal of the Quekett Microscopical Club* Ser. 2 **6**

Royal Academy Catalogue 1972 *English Drawings and Watercolours 1550–1850 in the collection of Mr. & Mrs. Paul Mellon* (London: Royal Academy of Arts)

Ruskin, John *Works* Library Edition vol. 35

Russell, J Cunningham 1879 Description of a new form of camera lucida *Journal of the Royal Microscopical Society* **2**

Schornherr D E 1976 *Picturesque Quebec, 1826–1832* (Public Archives of Canada)

Schroeder, Dr Hugo 1883 On a new camera lucida *Journal of the Royal Microscopical Society* Ser. 2 **3**

—— 1884–6 Note *Journal of the Quekett Microscopical Club* Ser. 2 **6**

Bibliography

Schwarz, Heinrich 1966 *Vermeer and the Camera Obscura* (Pantheon)

Scourfield D J 1898–1900 Note on Ashe's camera lucida *Journal of the Quekett Microscopical Club* **7**

Seibert, Messrs 1902 *Catalogue*

Seibert and Krafft 1883 Small camera lucida *Journal of the Royal Microscopical Society* Ser. 2 **3**

Sendall, Sir Walter 1891 On an improved method of making Microscopical Measurements with the Camera Lucida *Journal of the Royal Microscopical Society* Ser. 2 **11**

Sheldrake T 1809, 1810 On the camera lucida *Nicholson's Journal (Journal of Natural Philosophy, Chemistry and the Arts)* **24, 25**

Smyth, Lt, RN and Lowe F 1836 *Narrative of a Journey from Lima to Para*

*Society of Arts, Transactions (*later *Journal)* 1853 Drawing instruments

—— 1873 Cornelius Varley, obituary

—— 1874 Varley testimonial

Society for the Diffusion of Useful Knowledge see *Library of Useful Knowledge* **22**

Speaight, George 1963 Professor Pepper's ghost *Actes du III Congrès International d'Histoire du Théatre, 1961* (Société d'Histoire du Théatre dans le Cadre des Activities de la Fédération Internationale pour la Recherche Théatrale) pp. 48–56

Spendlove F St George 1954 The Canadian water-colours of James Pattison Cockburn *Connoisseur* (April)

Spohr, Louis 1865 *Autobiography* (translated from the German) (reprint 1969 (New York: Da Capo))

Staniland L N 1952 *The Principles of Line Illustration* (Burke)

Stanley W Ford 1888 *Descriptive Treatise on Mathematical Drawing Instruments*

—— 1925 Drawing and Mathematical Instruments

Stephanides T 1947 *The Microscope* (Faber)

Stothard, Mrs C A 1823 *Memoir . . . of C. A. Stothard, F.S.A.*

Suffolk W T 1869 On some of the means of delineating microscopic objects *Journal of the Quekett Microscopical Club* **1**

—— 1870 *On Microscopical Manipulation*

Swan, Henry 1863 On a new kind of miniature, possessing apparent solidity by means of a combination of prisms in contact therewith *British Journal of Photography*

—— 1864 The crystal miniature explained *ibid.*

—— 1866 Letters to the Editor *ibid.*

—— 1872 Letter to the Editor *ibid.*

—— *British Patents* No 559 (1860); No. 3249 (1862), No 2644 (1858), No 2020 (1859)

Swan Wm 1861 On the gradual production of luminous impressions on the eye *Transactions of the Royal Society of Edinburgh* **22**

Swift, Messrs 1879 Neutral tint camera lucida *Journal of the Royal Microscopical Society* **2**

Talbot W H Fox 1844 *Pencil of Nature* (reprint 1969 (New York: Da Capo))

Taylor E G R 1966 *Mathematical Practitioners of Hanoverian England, 1714–1840* (Institute of Navigation/Cambridge University Press)

Taylor T (ed) 1860 *Autobiographical Recollections by the late Charles Robert Leslie, R.A.*

Terquem A 1877 On the employment of a silvered glass as a camera lucida *London, Edinburgh and Dublin Philosophical Magazine* Ser. 5 **3**

Townsend G H 1877 *Manual of Dates*

Treacy J 1945 *Production Illustration*

Turner G L'E 1980 *Essays on the History of the Microscope* (Oxford: Senecio)

Varley, Cornelius Directions for using his Patent Graphic Telescope. Varley's own manuscript at the Whipple Museum of the History of Science, Cambridge. Printed version, nd. at the Science Museum, London. Inv. no. 1891–12

—— 1811 A new construction of a telescope, etc *British Patent* No 3430

—— 1836 Graphic Telescope *Journal of the Society of Arts* **50**

—— 1840 The Varley Graphic Telescope *Magazine of Science and School of Art* **2**

—— 1845 *On Optical Drawing Instruments*

—— 1849 On *Chara vulgaris, Transactions of the Microscopical Society* **2**

(——) 1873 Obituary *Illustrated London News* **63**

—— 1894 Note *Journal of the Quekett Microscopical Club* Ser. 2 **6**

Vecchi S 1868 Una nuova camera chiara *Nuovo Cimento* **28**

Wallis T E 1923 *Analytical Microscopy* (Arnold) (reprint 1957, Churchill)

—— 1955 Drawing from the Microscope *Journal of the Royal Microscopical Society* **75**

Walsh, John W T 1958 *Photometry* (Constable)

Ward, Hon Mrs Mary 1864, 1869 *Microscope Teachings*

Waterhouse, Maj. Gen. J 1909 Robert Hooke's portable camera obscura *Photographic Journal* **49**

Watson and Sons 1894 Abbe camera lucida in aluminium *Journal of the Royal Microscopical Society* Ser. 2 **14**

—— 1909, 1912 *Catalogues*

Bibliography

West, Francis 1831 *Description of the Camera Lucida . . . with the Observations of Capt Basil Hall, etc*

Willats J see Dubery F and Willats J

Wilson D G 1862 *Religio Chemici*

Wilson D J 1952 Home-made 'camera lucida' drawing aid *School Science Review* **33**

Winkel's small camera lucida 1883 *Journal of the Royal Microscopical Society* Ser. 2 **3**

Winkel's large drawing apparatus 1884 *Journal of the Royal Microscopical Society* Ser. 2 **4**

Wollaston, Wm Hyde 1803 On an Improvement in the Form of Spectacle Glasses *Philosophical Magazine* **18**

—— 1806 *British Patent* No 2993

—— 1807 Description of the camera lucida *Journal of Natural Philosophy, Chemistry and the Arts* **17** (also *Philosophical Magazine* **27**)

—— 1810 Beschreibung der Camera Lucida *Annalen der Physik* **34** (transl. von Gilbert)

—— 1812 On a periscopic camera obscura and microscope *Philosophical Transactions of the Royal Society* **102**

(——) 1829 Obituary *Gentleman's Magazine* Supplement to **99**

Wood, Rev J G 1861, 1900 *Common Objects of the Microscope*

Wynter H and Turner A 1975 *Scientific Instruments* (London: Studio Vista)

Yates R F and Yates M W 1954 *Early American Crafts and Hobbies*

Zantedeschi C F 1869–70 Della camera lucida di Wollaston *Atti del Istituto Veneto de Scienze* **15**

Zeiss, Messrs 1898, 1934 *Catalogues*

Index

Index